Contents

Introduction

Not Just Number combines mathematics and drawing in a unique and engaging way. By completing the activities in this resource, pupils practise and consolidate mathematical concepts and then use the answers as co-ordinates from which they draw various animals onto a square grid. In this way pupils come to see that mathematics is purposeful, and even those who think of themselves as poor drawers can gain great satisfaction from drawing many different types of animals – from a ladybird to a dinosaur. The activities are designed to be motivating and challenging for all pupils, including those who may be reluctant learners in mathematics.

Each activity centres on one animal and comprises two parts:

1. In the **maths co-ordinates** part, pupils write answers to mathematical questions across two strands of maths and nine topics within the strands. These answers are the co-ordinates for the second part.

2. In the **co-ordinate drawing** part, pupils use the co-ordinates to draw the animal on a square grid page. To add an element of surprise, the identity of the animal is not revealed to the pupils. However, this information is available to you in the table on the next page (as well as on the contents and answer pages).

You may decide on an animal at random for a mathematics class, or may choose a particular one to complement a current unit or theme. All pages can be photocopied for classroom use.

Content overview

The table on the next page provides a guide to the content of this resource. It will help you to choose an activity that suits the level of some or all of your pupils and/or that relates to concepts recently taught. The information is conveyed under the following headings:

*   **Maths strand** identifies which of two strands of mathematical content that the activity deals with, while **maths topic** identifies the topic within the strand, as follows:
    *   the strand of number covers the topics of addition and subtraction, multiplication tables, division, decimals and fractions, number study
    *   measurement covers the topics of time, mass, length, volume.

*   **Animal drawing** identifies the animal focused on for this activity. Your choice of animal could be based on a current class theme or unit.

*   **Drawing difficulty** provides a difficulty rating based on the complexity of the drawing, the number of co-ordinates needed to complete the drawing and the length of time needed to finish the drawing. With this information you can cater to individual pupil needs.

*   Each set of co-ordinates contains two numbers within a pair of brackets; the first is the *x* axis and the second is the *y* axis. **Grid axis** describes which of the co-ordinates are missing and which need to be found by answering mathematical questions, as follows:

Not Just Number

***Motivational maths
with animal grid drawings***
Years 5 to 7

Sylvia Cilas

essential
resources

Title:	Not Just Number Motivational maths with animal grid drawings Years 5 to 7
Author:	Sylvia Cilas
Editor:	Tanya Tremewan
Designer:	Michelle Peacock
Book Code:	260A
ISBN:	978-1-877498-45-9
Published:	2008
Publisher:	Essential Resources Educational Publishers Limited

United Kingdom Office:	New Zealand Office:	Australian Office:
Units 8–10 Parkside	PO Box 5036	PO Box 90
Shortgate Lane	Invercargill	Oak Flats
Laughton, BN8 6DG	ph: 0800 087 376	NSW 2529
ph: 0845 3636 147	fax: 0800 937 825	ph: 1800 005 068
fax: 0845 3636 148		fax: 1800 981 213

Websites:	www.erpublishers.com
Copyright:	Text: © Sylvia Cilas, 2008 Edition and Illustrations: © Essential Resources Educational Publishers Limited, 2008

About the author: Sylvia Cilas is a practising teacher with 16 years of experience in the primary school sector, along with a Diploma of Primary Teaching and a Bachelor of Education. She currently teaches at a primary school in Queensland, Australia. This is her third published book, designed specifically for teachers to use in the classroom. The inspiration for her books comes from her own pupils, who road-test her ideas and creations. She enjoys reading, tennis, running, dancing, rambling and, of course, creating books.

- – "x and y" means pupils work out two maths sums to create two numbers in each pair of brackets
- – "x or y" means pupils work out one maths sum for each pair of brackets, but it could be x or y
- – "x only" means pupils work out one maths sum for the x axis only because the y co-ordinate is given already
- – "y only" means pupils work out one maths sum for the y axis only because the x co-ordinate is given already.

For a more detailed overview of the mathematical content, see the second table. This information will also help you to choose an activity that will enable your pupils to practise and consolidate a particular mathematical strand or topic within each strand.

Teacher guide to content

Maths topic	Animal drawing (and activity number)	Drawing level	Grid axis
Multiplication tables	Dolphin (1)	Easy	x and y
	Horse (12)	Medium	x and y
	Elephant (10)	Medium	x and y
Decimals and fraction	Emu (3)	Easy	x or y
	Bear (5)	Medium	x only
Time	Fish (4)	Easy	y only
Division	Duck (2)	Easy	x or y
	Tiger (14)	Medium	x only
Addition and subtraction	Caterpillar (7)	Medium	x or y
	Frog (11)	Medium	y only
Mixed maths (ie, a mix of all maths topics)	Butterfly (16)	Hard	x or y
	Cat (6)	Medium	x or y
	Bee (15)	Hard	x or y
	Koala (13)	Medium	y only
	Dog (9)	Medium	x or y
	Ladybird (17)	Hard	x or y
Mass, volume and length	Dinosaur (8)	Medium	x only

Overview of mathematical content

Topic	Content	Terms or symbols	Examples
Addition and subtraction	Basic addition and subtraction facts	*sum, less than, more than, double, triple, add, minus, take, lots of*	• The sum of 13 and 5 is … • 8 more than 9 is … • Take 8 from 12. • 15 minus 8 equals … • Double 7 is … • 5 less than 14 is …
Multiplication tables	Basic times tables	*multiply, product, times*	• The product of 3 and 5 is … • 2 x 5 = __ • Multiply 4 by 7. • 6 x 3 = __
Division	Basic division facts	*divide, division, quotient*	• Divide 10 by 2. • 3$\overline{)15}$ • The quotient of 12 and 3 is … • 9 ÷ 3 = __
Decimals and fractions	Additng and subtracting decimals, finding fractions of numbers	*half, halve, third, quarter, fifth, sixth*	• One third of 12 is … • One third of 15 is … • Half of 20 is … • Half of 12 is … • 2.5 + 1.5 = __ • 8.6 minus 2.6 = __
Understanding numbers	Prime numbers, composite numbers, factors, square root, squared numbers, multiples		• Which is prime: 7 or 9? • Which is composite: 11 or 12? • Factors of 9 = 1, 3 and __ • The square root of 25 is … • The third multiple of 4 is …
Time	Various time intervals, digital time	*minute, hour, day, week, fortnight, month, year, decade, century, digital*	• How many hours are there between 3 pm and 6 pm? • How many hours are there in half a day? • How many minutes are there between 2:34 and 2:45? • How many months are there in a year? • 3 weeks = __ days
Mass	Kilograms, grams	*g, kg*	• 2000 g = __ kg • __ kg = 4000 g
Length	Millimetres, centimetres, metres	*mm, cm, m*	• 20 mm = __ cm • 500 cm = __ m
Volume	Millimetres, litres	*ml, l*	• 3000 ml = __ l • __ l = 5000 ml

How to use this resource

Here are some ideas for familiarising pupils with the basic procedure to follow for each activity. They will quickly learn what to do and look forward to the challenge of drawing a new animal.

Plotting co-ordinates

The co-ordinates are a set of two numbers in brackets, which are used on numeric square grids:

- The first number is found on the horizontal line (the x axis).
- The second number is found on the vertical line (the y axis).

Pupils join co-ordinates together by drawing lines with a ruler. They join each new dot to the previous one, except when the waves ⁓ appear. The waves indicate the end of this series of co-ordinates; the next co-ordinates do not join to the ones before the symbol so pupils must start a new line on another part of the grid. Some designs in this book are completed using one continuous line, while others are made up of a series of many lines.

Starting off

Before your pupils begin independent work on an activity, familiarise them with plotting co-ordinates. Begin with simple 2D shapes such as squares, rectangles and triangles, and then progress to simple designs and drawings so that pupils can practise basic skills before trying the more complicated designs in this book.

Set up this simple activity on the board. Ask your pupils to follow these directions to plot the co-ordinates (3, 5):

1. Find the number 3 on the x axis.
2. Find the number 5 on the y axis.
3. Put a dot where the grid line going up from 3 meets the grid line going across from 5.

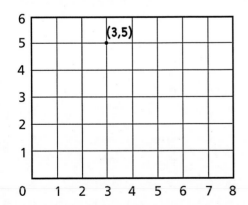

Correcting mathematical answers

After your pupils have calculated the answers to the mathematical questions (in the first part of the activity, "Maths co-ordinates"), check all answers for accuracy. This step is important to ensure that the animal drawings will be drawn correctly in the second part of the activity ("Co-ordinate drawing"). All answers (including the identity of each animal) are provided in the back of this resource.

© Essential Resources Educational Publishers Ltd, 2008

Activity 1

Drawing level: EASY

Maths topic: **Multiplication tables**
Axis: *x* and *y*

Maths co-ordinates

In each pair of brackets below, you will make the two co-ordinates that you need to draw a mystery animal on a square grid. Find the co-ordinates by working out the answers to the pair of multiplication tables. Write the two answers on the two lines inside the brackets (with the first answer on the first line and the second answer on the second line).

Co-ordinates

3 × 3 = ___	1 × 17 = ___	1. (___ , ___)
1 × 9 = ___	3 × 7 = ___	2. (___ , ___)
5 × 2 = ___	11 × 2 = ___	3. (___ , ___)
10 × 1 = ___	23 × 1 = ___	4. (___ , ___)
3 × 3 = ___	23 × 1 = ___	5. (___ , ___)
2 × 4 = ___	2 × 11 = ___	6. (___ , ___)
7 × 1 = ___	22 × 1 = ___	7. (___ , ___)
3 × 2 = ___	7 × 3 = ___	8. (___ , ___)
1 × 5 = ___	1 × 19 = ___	9. (___ , ___)
2 × 2 = ___	4 × 4 = ___	10. (___ , ___)
1 × 4 = ___	2 × 7 = ___	11. (___ , ___)
1 × 3 = ___	13 × 1 = ___	12. (___ , ___)
2 × 1 = ___	1 × 11 = ___	13. (___ , ___)
2 × 2 = ___	11 × 1 = ___	14. (___ , ___)
5 × 1 = ___	2 × 5 = ___	15. (___ , ___)
4 × 2 = ___	2 × 2 = ___	16. (___ , ___)
3 × 3 = ___	3 × 1 = ___	17. (___ , ___)
1 × 8 = ___	1 × 2 = ___	18. (___ , ___)
4 × 2 = ___	1 × 1 = ___	19. (___ , ___)
2 × 5 = ___	2 × 1 = ___	20. (___ , ___)
11 × 1 = ___	1 × 1 = ___	21. (___ , ___)
3 × 4 = ___	1 × 1 = ___	22. (___ , ___)
5 × 2 = ___	1 × 5 = ___	23. (___ , ___)
3 × 3 = ___	2 × 4 = ___	24. (___ , ___)
2 × 4 = ___	5 × 2 = ___	25. (___ , ___)

Co-ordinates

1 × 8 = ___	4 × 3 = ___	26. (___ , ___)
1 × 9 = ___	7 × 2 = ___	27. (___ , ___)
2 × 4 = ___	3 × 5 = ___	28. (___ , ___)
3 × 3 = ___	2 × 7 = ___	29. (___ , ___)
5 × 2 = ___	7 × 2 = ___	30. (___ , ___)
10 × 1 = ___	5 × 3 = ___	31. (___ , ___)
1 × 9 = ___	1 × 17 = ___	32. (___ , ___)
4 × 2 = ___	6 × 3 = ___	33. (___ , ___)
1 × 11 = ___	2 × 4 = ___	34. (___ , ___)
13 × 1 = ___	8 × 1 = ___	35. (___ , ___)
11 × 1 = ___	5 × 2 = ___	36. (___ , ___)
1 × 11 = ___	11 × 1 = ___	37. (___ , ___)
3 × 4 = ___	12 × 1 = ___	38. (___ , ___)
1 × 13 = ___	1 × 11 = ___	39. (___ , ___)
13 × 1 = ___	5 × 2 = ___	40. (___ , ___)
1 × 11 = ___	4 × 2 = ___	41. (___ , ___)
13 × 1 = ___	17 × 1 = ___	42. (___ , ___)
3 × 5 = ___	17 × 1 = ___	43. (___ , ___)
1 × 13 = ___	1 × 19 = ___	44. (___ , ___)
13 × 1 = ___	5 × 4 = ___	45. (___ , ___)
7 × 2 = ___	7 × 3 = ___	46. (___ , ___)
5 × 3 = ___	4 × 5 = ___	47. (___ , ___)
3 × 5 = ___	19 × 1 = ___	48. (___ , ___)
1 × 13 = ___	1 × 17 = ___	49. (___ , ___)

IMPORTANT NOTE:
Ask your teacher to check your answers before you use these co-ordinates to draw the animal on the next page. All your answers must be correct *before* you draw the animal.

Co-ordinate drawing

Draw a mystery animal using the co-ordinates that you have created by answering the maths questions. Follow these steps to plot the co-ordinates:

1. For each set of co-ordinates, look along the horizontal line to find the first number in the brackets.

2. Look along the vertical line to find the second number in the brackets.

3. Draw a dot on the point where the two gridlines from these numbers meet.

4. Join one dot to the next by ruling a line.

5. Start to draw a new line each time you get to some waves ~~~~~.

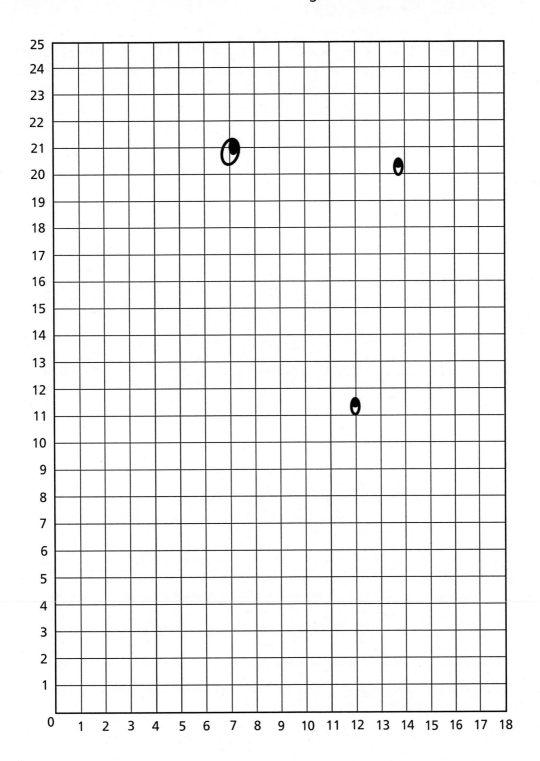

Activity 2

Maths topic: **Division**
Axis: **x or y**

Maths co-ordinates

In each pair of brackets below, you have been given one co-ordinate that will help you to draw a mystery animal on a square grid. But to draw the animal properly, you will need to find the other co-ordinate by working out the answer to the maths question. Write the answer on the blank line inside the pair of brackets.

	Co-ordinates		**Co-ordinates**
33 ÷ 3 = ___	1. (___, 17)	6)30	22. (___, 7)
160 ÷ 10 = ___	2. (13, ___)	The quotient of 21 and 3 is ...	23. (11, ___)
2)36	3. (___, 16)	140 ÷ 10 = ___	24. (___, 10)
17 ÷ 1 = ___	4. (18, ___)	1300 ÷ 100 = ___	25. (14, ___)
150 ÷ 10 = ___	5. (___, 18)	Divide 26 by 2.	26. (___, 16)
200 ÷ 10 = ___	6. (13, ___)	The quotient of 28 and 2 is ...	27. (___, 17)
Divide 22 by 2.	7. (___, 20)	160 ÷ 10 = ___	28. (16, ___)
The quotient of 100 and 10 is ...	8. (___, 18)	4)28	29. (7, ___)
5)50	9. (___, 17)	700 ÷ 100 = ___	30. (___, 5)
1500 ÷ 100 = ___	10. (11, ___)	Divide 16 by 4.	31. (8, ___)
88 ÷ 8 = ___	11. (___, 14)	3)27	32. (___, 4)
80 ÷ 8 = ___	12. (___, 13)	2)18	33. (___, 5)
2)14	13. (___, 14)	The quotient of 30 and 6 is ...	34. (8, ___)
Divide 25 by 5.	14. (___, 14)	3)24	35. (___, 7)
The quotient of 20 and 10 is ...	15. (___, 13)	10)100	36. (___, 7)
6 ÷ 6 = ___	16. (___, 14)	Divide 36 by 6.	37. (10, ___)
2)30	17. (1, ___)	110 ÷ 10 = ___	38. (___, 5)
10 ÷ 0 = ___	18. (___, 14)	500 ÷ 100 = ___	39. (12, ___)
5)0	19. (___, 13)	The quotient of 24 and 4 is ...	40. (12, ___)
4)36	20. (2, ___)	55 ÷ 5 = ___	41. (___, 6)
Divide 18 by 6.	21. (___, 8)	3)21	42. (11, ___)

IMPORTANT NOTE:
Ask your teacher to check your answers before you use these co-ordinates to draw the animal on the next page. All your answers must be correct *before* you draw the animal.

Co-ordinate drawing

Draw a mystery animal using the co-ordinates that you have created by answering the maths questions. Follow these steps to plot the co-ordinates:

1. For each set of co-ordinates, look along the horizontal line to find the first number in the brackets.

2. Look along the vertical line to find the second number in the brackets.

3. Draw a dot on the point where the two gridlines from these numbers meet.

4. Join one dot to the next by ruling a line.

5. Start to draw a new line each time you get to some waves ~~~~~~.

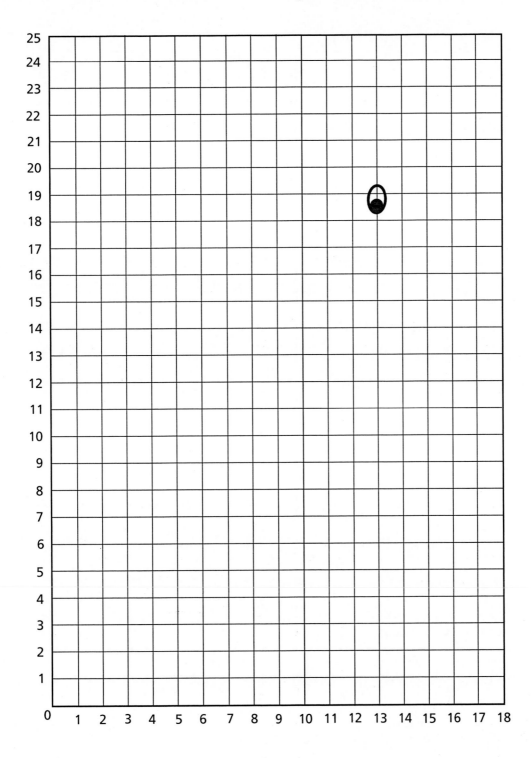

© Essential Resources Educational Publishers Ltd, 2008

Activity 3

Maths topic: **Decimals and fractions**
Axis: **x or y**

Maths co-ordinates

In each pair of brackets below, you have been given one co-ordinate that will help you to draw a mystery animal on a square grid. But to draw the animal properly, you will need to find the other co-ordinate by working out the answer to the maths question. Write the answer on the blank line inside the pair of brackets.

	Co-ordinates		Co-ordinates
3.4 + 5.6 = __	1. (0, ___)	$\frac{1}{5}$ of 40 is …	20. (___ , 9)
$\frac{1}{3}$ of 27 is …	2. (13, ___)	One third of 6 is …	21. (8, ___)
Half of 24 is …	3. (15, ___)	4.8 + 5.2 = __	22. (___ , 2)
Three quarters of 20 is …	4. (___ , 19)	3 + 6.0 = __	23. (___ , 3)
20.8 – 1.8 = __	5. (17, ___)	4.2 + 4.8 = __	24. (9, ___)
2.5 × 6 = __	6. (___ , 21)	0.7 + 0.3 = __	25. (___ , 9)
Half of 42 is …	7. (14, ___)	5.9 – 3.9 = __	26. (___ , 12)
Half of 26 is …	8. (___ , 20)	One third of 9 is …	27. (___ , 10)
15.8 – 2.8 = __	9. (___ , 14)	$\frac{1}{3}$ of 12 is …	28. (___ , 14)
½ of 30 is …	10. (10, ___)	4.5 + 5.5 = __	29. (5, ___)
One third of 15 is …	11. (___ , 15)	Half of 28 is …	30. (6, ___)
One quarter of 12 is …	12. (___ , 14)	10.8 – 3.8 = __	31. (___ , 10)
14.5 + –2.5 = __	13. (1, ___)	Two thirds of 12 is …	32. (___ , 14)
10.3 – 1.3 = __	14. (0, ___)	$\frac{2}{4}$ of 20 is …	33. (9, ___)
$\frac{1}{3}$ of 18 is …	15. (___ , 9)	One quarter of 40 is …	34. (___ , 14)
One fifth of 5 is …	16. (6, ___)	One third of 27 is …	35. (11, ___)
10.8 – 2.8 = __	17. (___ , 1)	9.3 + 2.7 = __	36. (___ , 13)
1.4 + 0.6 = __	18. (7, ___)	$\frac{1}{10}$ of 100 is …	37. (13, ___)
$\frac{1}{4}$ of 36 is …	19. (7, ___)	9.3 + 4.7 = __	38. (___ , 15)

IMPORTANT NOTE:
Ask your teacher to check your answers before you use these co-ordinates to draw the animal on the next page. All your answers must be correct *before* you draw the animal.

Co-ordinate drawing

Draw a mystery animal using the co-ordinates that you have created by answering the maths questions. Follow these steps to plot the co-ordinates:

1. For each set of co-ordinates, look along the horizontal line to find the first number in the brackets.

2. Look along the vertical line to find the second number in the brackets.

3. Draw a dot on the point where the two gridlines from these numbers meet.

4. Join one dot to the next by ruling a line.

5. Start to draw a new line each time you get to some waves ~~~~~~.

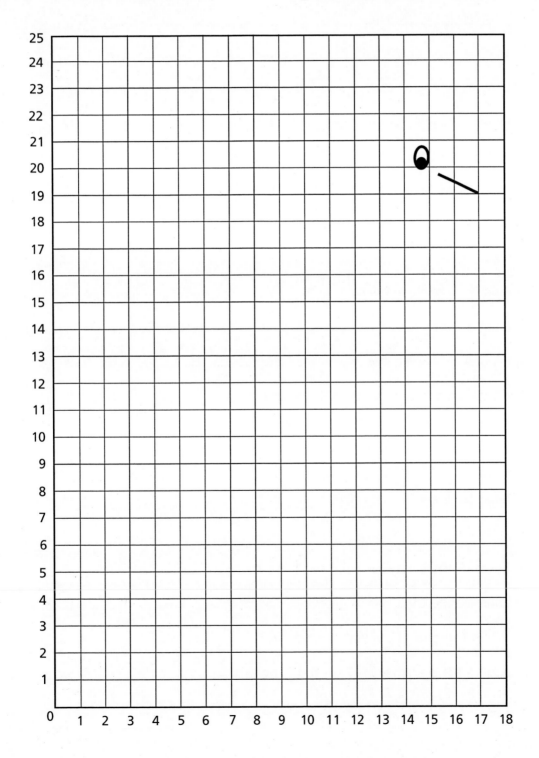

Activity 4

Maths topic: **Time**
Axis: *y only*

Maths co-ordinates

In each pair of brackets below, you have been given the first co-ordinate (on the *x* axis) that will help you to draw a mystery animal on a square grid. But to draw the animal properly, you will need to find the second co-ordinate (on the *y* axis) by working out the answer to the maths question. Write the answer on the blank line inside the pair of brackets.

Co-ordinates

Quarter of an hour = __ minutes .... 1. (13, ____)

How many minutes are there between 3:45 and 4:00?................................. 2. (15, ____)

How many minutes are there between 10:36 and 10:49?............................. 3. (17, ____)

How many minutes are there between 9:28 and 9:39?................................. 4. (18, ____)

How many minutes are there between 11:09 and 11:26?............................. 5. (17, ____)

How many minutes are there between 6:16 and 6:35?................................. 6. (14, ____)

3 weeks = __ days .... 7. (13, ____)

How many months are there in 2 years?... 8. (10, ____)

How many hours are there in a day?... 9. (9, ____)

How many minutes are there between 7:35 and 7:56?............................... 10. (6, ____)

How many months are there in one and a half years?................................ 11. (5, ____)

How many minutes are there between 2:19 and 2:33?............................... 12. (5, ____)

How many minutes are there between 8:52 and 9:03?............................... 13. (6, ____)

How many hours are there between 10:00 pm and 6:00 am? .... 14. (9, ____)

How many months are there in half a year?... 15. (8, ____)

How many hours are there between 6 pm and 10 pm?................................ 16. (5, ____)

How many hours are there between 4:50 pm and 8:50 pm?....................... 17. (2, ____)

How many minutes are there between 8:59 and 9:00?............................... 18. (5, ____)

How many hours are there between 11 am and 12 noon?........................... 19. (8, ____)

CONTINUED ON THE FOLLOWING PAGE

Activity 4

CONTINUED FROM THE PREVIOUS PAGE

Co-ordinates

200 years = ___ centuries .... 20. (10, ___)

How many minutes are there between 2:49 and 2:50? .... 21. (12, ___)

How many hours are there between 12 noon and 1 pm? .... 22. (15, ___)

One third of 12 days is … .... 23. (18, ___)

How many minutes are there between 7:58 and 8:02? .... 24. (15, ___)

How many hours are there between 2 am and 8 am? .... 25. (12, ___)

How many hours are there between 7 pm and 3 am? .... 26. (11, ___)

How many minutes are there between 4:47 and 4:58? .... 27. (13, ___)

2 weeks = ___ days .... 28. (14, ___)

How many minutes are there between 8:30 and 8:45? .... 29. (14, ___)

How many minutes are there between 2:48 and 3:02? .... 30. (14, ___)

How many minutes are there between 10:19 and 10:32? .... 31. (15, ___)

How many hours are there between 12 midnight and 11:00 am? .... 32. (16, ___)

How many minutes are there between 7:58 and 8:12? .... 33. (16, ___)

How many years are there in 2 decades? .... 34. (5, ___)

How many minutes are there between 4:20 and 4:39? .... 35. (3, ___)

How many minutes are there between 6:50 and 7:07? .... 36. (1, ___)

A fortnight = ___ days .... 37. (0, ___)

How many hours are there in half a day? .... 38. (0, ___)

Three quarters of 12 months is … .... 39. (1, ___)

How many minutes are there between 3:56 and 4:07? .... 40. (2, ___)

1 year = ___ months .... 41. (3, ___)

One third of 33 minutes is … .... 42. (6, ___)

 IMPORTANT NOTE:
Ask your teacher to check your answers before you use these co-ordinates to draw the animal on the next page. All your answers must be correct *before* you draw the animal.

Co-ordinate drawing

Draw a mystery animal using the co-ordinates that you have created by answering the maths questions. Follow these steps to plot the co-ordinates:

1. For each set of co-ordinates, look along the horizontal line to find the first number in the brackets.

2. Look along the vertical line to find the second number in the brackets.

3. Draw a dot on the point where the two gridlines from these numbers meet.

4. Join one dot to the next by ruling a line.

5. Start to draw a new line each time you get to some waves 〰️.

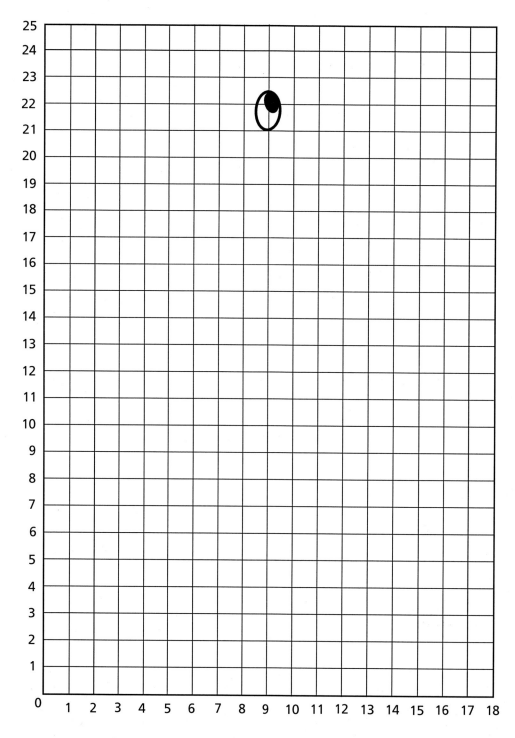

Activity 5

Drawing level: MEDIUM

Maths topic: **Decimals and fractions**
Axis: **x only**

Maths co-ordinates

In each pair of brackets below, you have been given the second co-ordinate (on the *y* axis) that will help you to draw a mystery animal on a square grid. But to draw the animal properly, you will need to find the first co-ordinate (on the *x* axis) by working out the answer to the maths question. Write the answer on the blank line inside the pair of brackets.

	Co-ordinates		**Co-ordinates**
2.5 + 3.5 = __	1. (____, 21)	8.7 – 6.7 = __	33. (____, 7)
$\frac{1}{3}$ of 9 is …	2. (____, 18)	One quarter of 12 is …	34. (____, 8)
2.4 + 0.6 = __	3. (____, 14)	Two fifths of 10 is …	35. (____, 10)
7.5 – 1.5 = __	4. (____, 12)	0.5 + 3.5 = __	36. (____, 7)
$\frac{1}{3}$ of 33	5. (____, 12)	Half of 26 is …	37. (____, 13)
Half of 28 is …	6. (____, 14)	Half of 30 is …	38. (____, 12)
12.5 + 1.5 = __	7. (____, 18)	10.2 + 5.8 = __	39. (____, 10)
8.3 + 2.7 = __	8. (____, 21)	Half of 32 is …	40. (____, 8)
One third of 18 is …	9. (____, 21)	($\frac{1}{3}$ of 15) + ($\frac{1}{2}$ of 20) = __	41. (____, 7)
2 + 3.0 = __	10. (____, 22)	11.5 + 2.5 = __	42. (____, 8)
$\frac{1}{10}$ of 40	11. (____, 22)	9.6 + 3.4 = __	43. (____, 10)
5.9 – 3.9 = __	12. (____, 20)	7.5 + 5.5 = __	44. (____, 7)
1.4 + 0.6 = __	13. (____, 19)	$\frac{1}{5}$ of 55 is …	45. (____, 7)
$\frac{1}{4}$ of 12 is …	14. (____, 18)	One quarter of 40 is …	46. (____, 5)
One quarter of 44 is …	15. (____, 21)	2.5 × 4 = __	47. (____, 3)
8.5 + 3.5 = __	16. (____, 22)	$\frac{1}{8}$ of 88 is …	48. (____, 1)
3.7 + 8.3 + 1.0 = __	17. (____, 22)	8.4 + 5.6 = __	49. (____, 1)
$\frac{3}{4}$ of 20 is …	18. (____, 20)	20.5 – 5.5 = __	50. (____, 3)
20.8 – 5.8 = __	19. (____, 19)	Half of 30 is …	51. (____, 5)
9.2 + 4.8 = __	20. (____, 18)	8.6 + 5.4 = __	52. (____, 7)
$\frac{1}{3}$ of 21 is …	21. (____, 12)	$\frac{1}{9}$ of 99 is …	53. (____, 7)
One quarter of 24 is …	22. (____, 13)	$\frac{1}{8}$ of 24 is …	54. (____, 7)
$\frac{1}{6}$ of 36 is …	23. (____, 15)	7.7 – 5.7 = __	55. (____, 5)
3.4 + 3.6 = __	24. (____, 16)	1.5 + 0.5 = __	56. (____, 3)
Two quarters of 20 is …	25. (____, 16)	0.5 + 2.5 = __	57. (____, 1)
$\frac{1}{6}$ of 66 is …	26. (____, 15)	One quarter of 24 is …	58. (____, 1)
Half of 22 is …	27. (____, 13)	$\frac{1}{4}$ of 28 is …	59. (____, 3)
One third of 30 is …	28. (____, 12)	Half of 14 is …	60. (____, 5)
$\frac{1}{3}$ of 12 is …	29. (____, 13)	One fifth of 30 is …	61. (____, 7)
6.8 – 4.8 = __	30. (____, 12)	$\frac{1}{10}$ of 30 is …	62. (____, 7)
$\frac{1}{5}$ of 5 is …	31. (____, 10)	One eleventh of 77 is …	63. (____, 3)
0.4 + 0.6 = __	32. (____, 8)	$\frac{1}{5}$ of 50 is …	64. (____, 3)

IMPORTANT NOTE:
Ask your teacher to check your answers before you use these co-ordinates to draw the animal on the next page. All your answers must be correct *before* you draw the animal.

Co-ordinate drawing

Draw a mystery animal using the co-ordinates that you have created by answering the maths questions. Follow these steps to plot the co-ordinates:

1. For each set of co-ordinates, look along the horizontal line to find the first number in the brackets.

2. Look along the vertical line to find the second number in the brackets.

3. Draw a dot on the point where the two gridlines from these numbers meet.

4. Join one dot to the next by ruling a line.

5. Start to draw a new line each time you get to some waves ⌇⌇⌇⌇⌇.

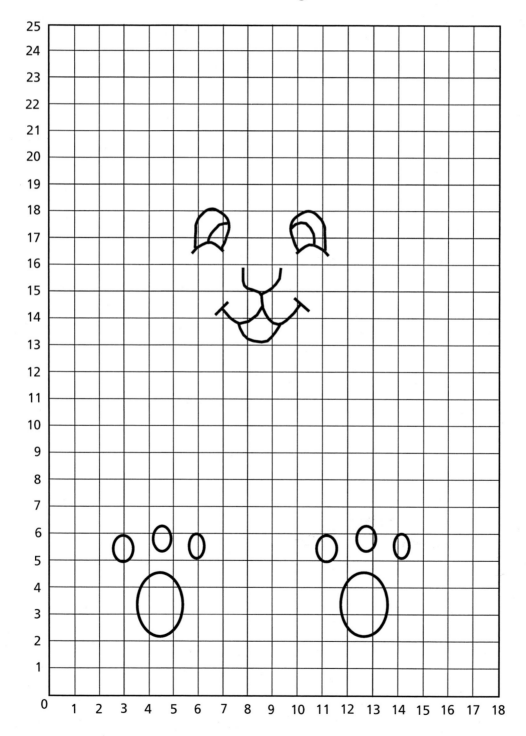

Activity 6

Maths topic: **Mixed maths**
Axis: **x or y**

Maths co-ordinates

In each pair of brackets below, you have been given the second co-ordinate (on the y axis) that will help you to draw a mystery animal on a square grid. But to draw the animal properly, you will need to find the first co-ordinate (on the x axis) by working out the answer to the maths question. Write the answer on the blank line inside the pair of brackets.

	Co-ordinates		**Co-ordinates**
3 squared equals ...	1. (____, 19)	The sum of 10 and 8 is ...	19. (3, ____)
Subtract 13 from 30.	1. (2, ____)	$\frac{1}{3}$ of 12 is ...	20. (____, 21)
6 more than 7 is ...	3. (2, ____)	The third multiple of 6 is ...	21. (5, ____)
$6 \div 6 =$ __	4. (____, 11)	Halve 36.	22. (12, ____)
7000 g = __ kg	5. (1, ____)	__ days = 1 fortnight	23. (____, 24)
$22 \div 11 =$ __	6. (____, 5)	8 less than 25 is ...	24. (16, ____)
$2.5 + 3.5 =$ __	7. (____, 1)	$3\overline{)39}$	25. (____, 18)
$\frac{1}{2}$ of 24 is ...	8. (____, 1)	Halve 42.	26. (14, ____)
One fifth of 25 is ...	9. (16, ____)	How many minutes are there between 8:15 and 8:30?	27. (____, 18)
$(6 \times 4) - 7 =$ __	10. (____, 7)	50 mm = __ cm	28. (____, 15)
$(5 \times 2) + (14 \div 2) =$ __	11. (____, 11)	__ kg = 6000 g	29. (____, 15)
21 minus 8 equals ...	12. (16, ____)	$10.5 - 3.5 =$ __	30. (____, 14)
4 squared is ...	13. (____, 17)	$3\overline{)21}$	31. (____, 12)
$(6 \times 3) \div 1 =$ __	14. (12, ____)	Which is prime: 8 or 11?	32. (6, ____)
$900 \div 100 =$ __	15. (____, 19)	The quotient of 10 and 2 is ...	33. (____, 11)
$(10 \div 2) + (3 \times 4) =$ __	16. (2, ____)	The square root of 16 is ...	34. (____, 12)
40 mm = __ cm	17. (____, 24)	4000 ml = __ l	35. (____, 14)
$6\overline{)36}$	18. (____, 18)	$(2 \times 4) + (5 + 2) =$ __	36. (5, ____)

CONTINUED ON THE FOLLOWING PAGE

CONTINUED FROM THE PREVIOUS PAGE

Co-ordinates ───────── Co-ordinates

How many minutes are there between 3:22 and 3:36?	37. (5, ____)
$^2/_3$ of 9 is ...	38. (____, 14)
Divide 18 by 3.	39. (____, 12)
$(5 \times 4) - 8 =$ __	40. (5, ____)
Which is composite: 13 or 14?	41. (5, ____)
$4000 - 3985 =$ __	42. (12, ____)
Halve 30.	43. (13, ____)
$3 + 8 + 3 =$ __	44. (____, 14)
The product of 7 and 2 is ...	45. (____, 12)
Subtract 10 from 23.	46. (____, 11)
18 minus 7 equals ...	47. (12, ____)
$120 \div 10 =$ __	48. (11, ____)
__ days = 2 weeks	49. (11, ____)
The fifth multiple of 3 is ...	50. (12, ____)
8 more than 6 is ...	51. (12, ____)
The product of 2 and 6 is ...	52. (____, 12)
Which is prime: 12 or 13?	53. (____, 12)
Halve 28.	54. (13, ____)
Subtract 9 from 21.	55. (____, 14)
Divide 15 by 3.	56. (5, ____)

$70 \div 10 =$ __	57. (____, 3)
$^1/_3$ of 33 is ...	58. (____, 3)
$7.5 - 2.5 =$ __	59. (13, ____)
__ cm = 30 mm	60. (9, ____)
How many minutes are there between 7:57 and 8:06?	61. (____, 7)
__ kg = 7000 g	62. (____, 9)
$8400 - 8390 =$ __	63. (9, ____)
Which is composite: 7 or 9?	64. (11, ____)
$5.4 + 3.6 =$ __	65. (____, 7)
$0 \div 8 =$ __	66. (____, 11)
$600 \div 100 =$ __	67. (____, 8)
Which is prime: 3 or 6?	68. (1, ____)
$3\overline{)24}$	69. (6, ____)
One third of 18 is ...	70. (0, ____)
$(5 \times 2) + (2 \times 4) =$ __	71. (____, 11)
The product of 3 and 4 is ...	72. (____, 8)
The quotient of 12 and 4 is ...	73. (17, ____)
The third multiple of 4 is ...	74. (____, 8)
Subtract 8 from 26.	75. (____, 6)

IMPORTANT NOTE:
Ask your teacher to check your answers before you use these co-ordinates to draw the animal on the next page. All your answers must be correct *before* you draw the animal.

Co-ordinate drawing

Draw a mystery animal using the co-ordinates that you have created by answering the maths questions. Follow these steps to plot the co-ordinates:

1. For each set of co-ordinates, look along the horizontal line to find the first number in the brackets.

2. Look along the vertical line to find the second number in the brackets.

3. Draw a dot on the point where the two gridlines from these numbers meet.

4. Join one dot to the next by ruling a line.

5. Start to draw a new line each time you get to some waves ∼∼∼∼∼.

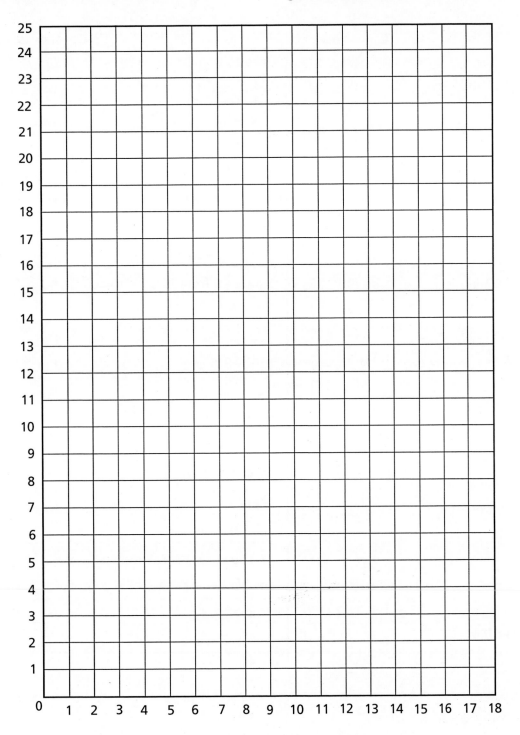

© Essential Resources Educational Publishers Ltd, 2008

Activity 7

Maths topic: **Addition and subtraction**
Axis: ***x* or *y***

Maths co-ordinates

In each pair of brackets below, you have been given one co-ordinate that will help you to draw a mystery animal on a square grid. But to draw the animal properly, you will need to find the other co-ordinate by working out the answer to the maths question. Write the answer on the blank line inside the pair of brackets.

	Co-ordinates		**Co-ordinates**
7 + 9 + 5 = __	1. (9, ___)	Take 10 from 33	26. (8, ___)
The sum of 18 and 5 is …	2. (8, ___)	The sum of 12 and 9 is …	27. (7, ___)
17 + 7 = __	3. (7, ___)	The sum of 8 and 10 is …	28. (6, ___)
14 – (5 + 3) = __	4. (___, 24)	8 + 6 + 7 = __	29. (9, ___)
8 less than 12 is …	5. (___, 23)	Take 9 from 18.	30. (___, 17)
82 – 79 = __	6. (___, 21)	11 less than 30 is …	31. (11, ___)
7300 – 7280 = __	7. (3, ___)	The sum of 7 and 9 is …	32. (10, ___)
3 + 7 + 9 = __	8. (4, ___)	(9 + 8) – 1 = __	33. (13, ___)
2 + (12 – 8) = __	9. (___, 18)	Subtract 6 from 15.	34. (___, 15)
The sum of 9 and 7 is …	10. (9, ___)	Double 7.	35. (12, ___)
(18 + 6) – 12 = __	11. (5, ___)	(7 + 8) – 1 = __	36. (7, ___)
Take 590 from 600.	12. (4, ___)	8300 – 8290 = __	37. (___, 11)
(12 + 5) – 9 = __	13. (5, ___)	3 + 5 + 3 = __	38. (5, ___)
5000 – 4990 = __	14. (___, 4)	Take 2990 from 3000.	39. (10, ___)
(30 + 20) – 49 = __	15. (10, ___)	192 less than 200 is …	40. (7, ___)
500 – (270 + 230) = __	16. (12, ___)	Take 16 from 26.	41. (___, 9)
800 – 798 = __	17. (13, ___)	Triple 3.	42. (___, 6)
The sum of 7 and 6 is …	18. (___, 6)	(18 + 3) – 10 = __	43. (___, 8)
Subtract 390 from 400.	19. (___, 9)	67 – 63 = __	44. (10, ___)
7 less than 18 is …	20. (10, ___)	Double 6.	45. (___, 6)
(12 + 7) – 6 = __	21. (___, 13)	7000 – 6990 = __	46. (___, 3)
(12 + 6) – 3 = __	22. (14, ___)	4800 – 4798 = __	47. (13, ___)
(7 + 8) – 3 = __	23. (___, 19)		
7 more than 14 is …	24. (10, ___)		
30 – 9 = __	25. (9, ___)		

IMPORTANT NOTE:
Ask your teacher to check your answers before you use these co-ordinates to draw the animal on the next page. All your answers must be correct *before* you draw the animal.

Co-ordinate drawing

Draw a mystery animal using the co-ordinates that you have created by answering the maths questions. Follow these steps to plot the co-ordinates:

1. For each set of co-ordinates, look along the horizontal line to find the first number in the brackets.

2. Look along the vertical line to find the second number in the brackets.

3. Draw a dot on the point where the two gridlines from these numbers meet.

4. Join one dot to the next by ruling a line.

5. Start to draw a new line each time you get to some waves ~~~~~~.

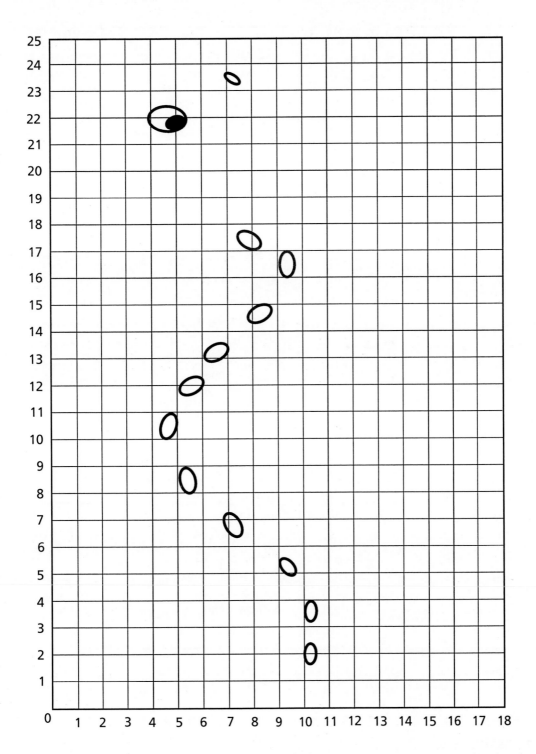

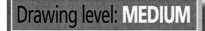

Activity 8

Maths topic: **Mass, volume and length**
Axis: *x only*

Maths co-ordinates

In each pair of brackets below, you have been given the second co-ordinate (on the *y* axis) that will help you to draw a mystery animal on a square grid. But to draw the animal properly, you will need to find the first co-ordinate (on the *x* axis) by working out the answer to the maths question. Write the answer on the blank line inside the pair of brackets.

	Co-ordinates		**Co-ordinates**
150 mm = ___ cm	1. (___, 10)	14,000 ml = ___ l	35. (___, 17)
140 mm = ___ cm	2. (___, 9)	1200 cm = ___ m	36. (___, 14)
___ cm = 130 mm	3. (___, 7)	1 cm = ___ mm	37. (___, 14)
9000 g = ___ kg	4. (___, 5)		
___ kg = 7000 g	5. (___, 5)	9 m + 5 m = ___ m	38. (___, 17)
___ l = 5000 ml	6. (___, 6)	30 g − 15 g = ___ g	39. (___, 14)
60 mm = ___ cm	7. (___, 4)	9 l + 6 l = ___ l	40. (___, 13)
___ kg = 6000 g	8. (___, 3)	8 kg + 7 kg = ___ kg	41. (___, 17)
50 mm = ___ cm	9. (___, 2)	___ m = 1600 cm	42. (___, 16)
400 cm = ___ m	10. (___, 3)	160 mm = ___ cm	43. (___, 14)
200 cm = ___ m	11. (___, 4)	1500 cm = ___ m	44. (___, 14)
1000 g = ___ kg	12. (___, 6)	800 cm + 600 cm = ___ m	45. (___, 13)
20 mm = ___ cm	13. (___, 8)	___ cm = 150 mm	46. (___, 13)
3 l + 4 l = ___ l	14. (___, 8)	11 kg + 6 kg = ___ kg	47. (___, 12)
8000 g = ___ kg	15. (___, 9)	170 mm = ___ cm	48. (___, 9)
___ m = 700 cm	16. (___, 11)	20 m − 5 m = ___ m	49. (___, 10)
600 cm = ___ m	17. (___, 12)	___ cm = 140 mm	50. (___, 10)
6000 g = ___ kg	18. (___, 17)	150 mm = ___ cm	51. (___, 10)
___ cm = 70 mm	19. (___, 18)	9 m + 7 m = ___ m	52. (___, 9)
80 mm = ___ cm	20. (___, 20)	___ cm = 160 mm	53. (___, 7)
___ l = 7000 ml	21. (___, 21)	140 mm = ___ cm	54. (___, 8)
8 kg − 3 kg = ___ kg	22. (___, 21)	80 mm = ___ cm	55. (___, 9)
___ kg = 3000 g	23. (___, 20)	600 cm = ___ m	56. (___, 9)
___ l = 1000 ml	24. (___, 17)	___ m = 700 cm	57. (___, 11)
5 g − 5 g = ___ g	25. (___, 17)	5000 g = ___ kg	58. (___, 11)
10 mm = ___ cm	26. (___, 20)	___ l = 6000 ml	59. (___, 13)
___ l = 2000 ml	27. (___, 21)	4000 g = ___ kg	60. (___, 14)
5000 g = ___ kg	28. (___, 23)	900 cm − 300 cm = ___ m	61. (___, 16)
5 cm + 4 cm = ___ cm	29. (___, 23)	___ m = 400 cm	62. (___, 17)
120 mm = ___ cm	30. (___, 22)	300 cm + 400 cm = ___ m	63. (___, 18)
7 m + 6 m = ___ m	31. (___, 20)	60 mm = ___ cm	64. (___, 19)
150 mm = ___ cm	32. (___, 20)	200 cm + 600 cm = ___ m	65. (___, 20)
___ cm = 160 mm	33. (___, 19)		
8 l + 8 l = ___ l	34. (___, 17)		

IMPORTANT NOTE:
Ask your teacher to check your answers before you use these co-ordinates to draw the animal on the next page. All your answers must be correct *before* you draw the animal.

Co-ordinate drawing

Draw a mystery animal using the co-ordinates that you have created by answering the maths questions. Follow these steps to plot the co-ordinates:

1. For each set of co-ordinates, look along the horizontal line to find the first number in the brackets.

2. Look along the vertical line to find the second number in the brackets.

3. Draw a dot on the point where the two gridlines from these numbers meet.

4. Join one dot to the next by ruling a line.

5. Start to draw a new line each time you get to some waves ～～～.

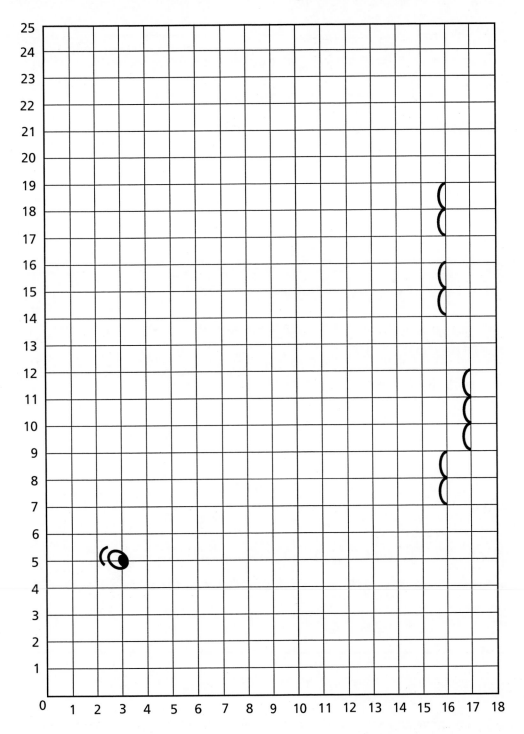

© Essential Resources Educational Publishers Ltd, 2008

Activity 9

Maths topic: **Mixed maths**
Axis: **x or y**

Maths co-ordinates

In each pair of brackets below, you have been given one co-ordinate that will help you to draw a mystery animal on a square grid. But to draw the animal properly, you will need to find the other co-ordinate by working out the answer to the maths question. Write the answer on the blank line inside the pair of brackets.

	Co-ordinates		**Co-ordinates**
$80 \div 8 =$ ___	1. (___, 22)	How many hours are there between 7:00 pm and 9:00 pm?	19. (___, 17)
$8 + 6 + 7 =$ ___	2. (9, ___)	4 squared is …	20. (4, ___)
The sum of 6 and 12 is …	3. (8, ___)	The quotient of 25 and 5 is …	21. (___, 16)
The square root of 49 is …	4. (___, 17)	$2\overline{)14}$	22. (___, 17)
Half of 30 is …	5. (7, ___)	___ months = 1 year	23. (___, 21)
$28 - (8 + 7) =$ ___	6. (9, ___)	$(3 \times 8) - 4 =$ ___	24. (14, ___)
19 minus 7 equals …	7. (___, 13)	$(20 \div 2) + 8 =$ ___	25. (15, ___)
$800 - 785 =$ ___	8. (14, ___)	Halve 32.	26. (___, 16)
How many minutes are there between 2:15 and 2:32?	9. (14, ___)	$(3 \times 4) + 3 =$ ___	27. (17, ___)
The sixth multiple of 3 is …	10. (13, ___)	170 mm = ___ cm	28. (___, 13)
Halve 42.	11. (12, ___)	How many hours are there in half a day?	29. (16, ___)
Which is prime: 8 or 11?	12. (___, 22)	$400 - 388 =$ ___	30. (14, ___)
How many hours are there between 3:00 pm and 1:00 am?	13. (___, 22)	$(8 \times 3) - 11 =$ ___	31. (___, 13)
One third of 27 is …	14. (___, 21)	How many days are there in 2 weeks?	32. (13, ___)
Multiply 7 by 3.	15. (8, ___)		
$800 - 780 =$ ___	16. (5, ___)		
$^1/_3$ of 9 is …	17. (___, 19)		
200 cm = ___ m	18. (___, 18)		

CONTINUED ON THE FOLLOWING PAGE

Activity 9

CONTINUED FROM THE PREVIOUS PAGE

Co-ordinates

8000 g = ___ kg	33. (___, 16)
3)$\overline{27}$	34. (___, 14)
(7 × 3) − 7 = ___	35. (12, ___)
The fourth multiple of 4 is ...	36. (13, ___)
Double 6.	37. (___, 13)
77 ÷ 7 = ___	38. (13, ___)
3.5 + 4.5 = ___	39. (13, ___)
___ days = 1 fortnight	40. (___, 6)
150 mm = ___ cm	41. (___, 5)
$\frac{1}{4}$ of 16 is ...	42. (15, ___)
55 ÷ 5 = ___	43. (___, 4)
2.7 + 6.3 = ___	44. (___, 8)
___ l = 9000 ml	45. (9, ___)
3 squared is ...	46. (11, ___)
How many minutes are there between 5:24 and 5:32?	47. (11, ___)
How many months are there in half a year?	48. (12, ___)
5000 g = ___ kg	49. (13, ___)
A baker's dozen is ...	50. (___, 4)
Divide 39 by 3.	51. (9, ___)
60 mm = ___ cm	52. (___, 12)
3000 − 2990 = ___	53. (4, ___)
___ cm = 90 mm	54. (3, ___)

Co-ordinates

2 kg + 5 kg = ___ kg	55. (2, ___)
6200 − 6195 = ___	56. (2, ___)
$\frac{1}{4}$ of 12 is ...	57. (___, 4)
4)$\overline{36}$	58. (___, 4)
___ l = 5000 ml	59. (9, ___)
10.8 − 4.8 = ___	60. (8, ___)
200 cm + 400 cm = ___ m	61. (5, ___)
___ cm = 70 mm	62. (___, 6)
700 ÷ 100 = ___	63. (8, ___)
The product of 3 and 3 is ...	64. (8, ___)
Which is composite: 7 or 10?	65. (6, ___)
How many hours are there between 3.00 am and 10.00 am?	66. (2, ___)
2.3 + 6.7 = ___	67. (2, ___)
How many minutes are there between 7:57 and 8:08?	68. (3, ___)
300 cm = ___ m	69. (___, 13)
9 more than 7 is ...	70. (2, ___)
10.2 + 5.8 = ___	71. (3, ___)
$\frac{2}{5}$ of 10	72. (___, 14)
___ years = 1 decade	73. (4, ___)
How many hours are there between 7:00 pm and 3:00 am?	74. (___, 6)
(5 + 8) − 7 = ___	75. (10, ___)

IMPORTANT NOTE:
Ask your teacher to check your answers before you use these co-ordinates to draw the animal on the next page. All your answers must be correct *before* you draw the animal.

Co-ordinate drawing

Draw a mystery animal using the co-ordinates that you have created by answering the maths questions. Follow these steps to plot the co-ordinates:

1. For each set of co-ordinates, look along the horizontal line to find the first number in the brackets.

2. Look along the vertical line to find the second number in the brackets.

3. Draw a dot on the point where the two gridlines from these numbers meet.

4. Join one dot to the next by ruling a line.

5. Start to draw a new line each time you get to some waves ～～～.

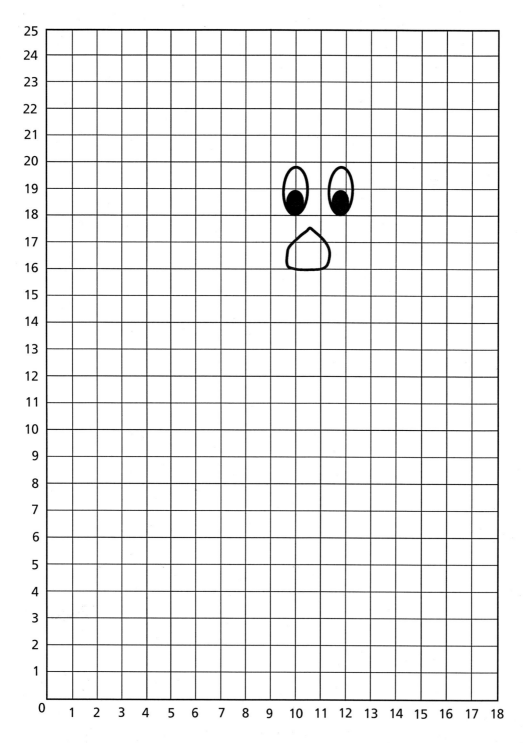

Activity 10

Maths topic: **Multiplication tables**
Axis: *x and y*

Maths co-ordinates

In each pair of brackets below, you will make the two co-ordinates that you need to draw a mystery animal on a square grid. Find the co-ordinates by working out the answers to the pair of multiplication tables. Write the two answers on the two lines inside the brackets (with the first answer on the first line and the second answer on the second line).

		Co-ordinates			**Co-ordinates**
2 × 2 = ___	3 × 4 = ___	1. (___ , ___)	4 × 3 = ___	3 × 2 = ___	32. (___ , ___)
1 × 3 = ___	13 × 1 = ___	2. (___ , ___)	7 × 2 = ___	5 × 1 = ___	33. (___ , ___)
3 × 1 = ___	4 × 4 = ___	3. (___ , ___)	4 × 4 = ___	2 × 3 = ___	34. (___ , ___)
1 × 5 = ___	6 × 3 = ___	4. (___ , ___)	2 × 8 = ___	2 × 2 = ___	35. (___ , ___)
5 × 1 = ___	19 × 1 = ___	5. (___ , ___)	3 × 4 = ___	4 × 1 = ___	36. (___ , ___)
2 × 2 = ___	5 × 4 = ___	6. (___ , ___)	2 × 5 = ___	1 × 3 = ___	37. (___ , ___)
1 × 1 = ___	3 × 7 = ___	7. (___ , ___)	3 × 3 = ___	3 × 1 = ___	38. (___ , ___)
1 × 1 = ___	2 × 11 = ___	8. (___ , ___)	1 × 7 = ___	2 × 2 = ___	39. (___ , ___)
5 × 1 = ___	7 × 3 = ___	9. (___ , ___)	3 × 2 = ___	1 × 5 = ___	40. (___ , ___)
3 × 2 = ___	4 × 5 = ___	10. (___ , ___)	5 × 1 = ___	1 × 7 = ___	41. (___ , ___)
7 × 1 = ___	2 × 9 = ___	11. (___ , ___)	1 × 5 = ___	3 × 3 = ___	42. (___ , ___)
1 × 7 = ___	17 × 1 = ___	12. (___ , ___)	13 × 1 = ___	2 × 7 = ___	43. (___ , ___)
2 × 4 = ___	6 × 3 = ___	13. (___ , ___)	7 × 2 = ___	14 × 1 = ___	44. (___ , ___)
3 × 3 = ___	5 × 3 = ___	14. (___ , ___)	3 × 5 = ___	1 × 15 = ___	45. (___ , ___)
1 × 11 = ___	5 × 3 = ___	15. (___ , ___)	5 × 3 = ___	1 × 13 = ___	46. (___ , ___)
13 × 1 = ___	4 × 4 = ___	16. (___ , ___)	3 × 4 = ___	13 × 1 = ___	47. (___ , ___)
2 × 7 = ___	2 × 8 = ___	17. (___ , ___)	5 × 1 = ___	1 × 13 = ___	48. (___ , ___)
4 × 4 = ___	1 × 17 = ___	18. (___ , ___)	2 × 2 = ___	3 × 4 = ___	49. (___ , ___)
8 × 2 = ___	3 × 5 = ___	19. (___ , ___)	4 × 1 = ___	2 × 5 = ___	50. (___ , ___)
7 × 2 = ___	5 × 3 = ___	20. (___ , ___)	5 × 1 = ___	3 × 3 = ___	51. (___ , ___)
4 × 3 = ___	13 × 1 = ___	21. (___ , ___)	2 × 4 = ___	9 × 1 = ___	52. (___ , ___)
6 × 2 = ___	3 × 4 = ___	22. (___ , ___)	3 × 3 = ___	5 × 2 = ___	53. (___ , ___)
13 × 1 = ___	2 × 5 = ___	23. (___ , ___)	1 × 9 = ___	4 × 3 = ___	54. (___ , ___)
1 × 13 = ___	4 × 2 = ___	24. (___ , ___)	2 × 4 = ___	13 × 1 = ___	55. (___ , ___)
6 × 2 = ___	3 × 2 = ___	25. (___ , ___)	3 × 2 = ___	1 × 13 = ___	56. (___ , ___)
11 × 1 = ___	5 × 1 = ___	26. (___ , ___)	1 × 5 = ___	3 × 4 = ___	57. (___ , ___)
3 × 4 = ___	2 × 3 = ___	27. (___ , ___)	5 × 1 = ___	5 × 2 = ___	58. (___ , ___)
2 × 7 = ___	3 × 2 = ___	28. (___ , ___)	4 × 2 = ___	2 × 5 = ___	59. (___ , ___)
5 × 3 = ___	1 × 7 = ___	29. (___ , ___)	8 × 1 = ___	4 × 3 = ___	60. (___ , ___)
3 × 5 = ___	2 × 3 = ___	30. (___ , ___)	1 × 7 = ___	13 × 1 = ___	61. (___ , ___)
2 × 7 = ___	1 × 5 = ___	31. (___ , ___)	3 × 3 = ___	1 × 3 = ___	62. (___ , ___)
			11 × 1 = ___	2 × 1 = ___	63. (___ , ___)

IMPORTANT NOTE:
Ask your teacher to check your answers before you use these co-ordinates to draw the animal on the next page. All your answers must be correct *before* you draw the animal.

© Essential Resources Educational Publishers Ltd, 2008

Co-ordinate drawing

Draw a mystery animal using the co-ordinates that you have created by answering the maths questions. Follow these steps to plot the co-ordinates:

1. For each set of co-ordinates, look along the horizontal line to find the first number in the brackets.
2. Look along the vertical line to find the second number in the brackets.
3. Draw a dot on the point where the two gridlines from these numbers meet.
4. Join one dot to the next by ruling a line.
5. Start to draw a new line each time you get to some waves ~~~~~~.

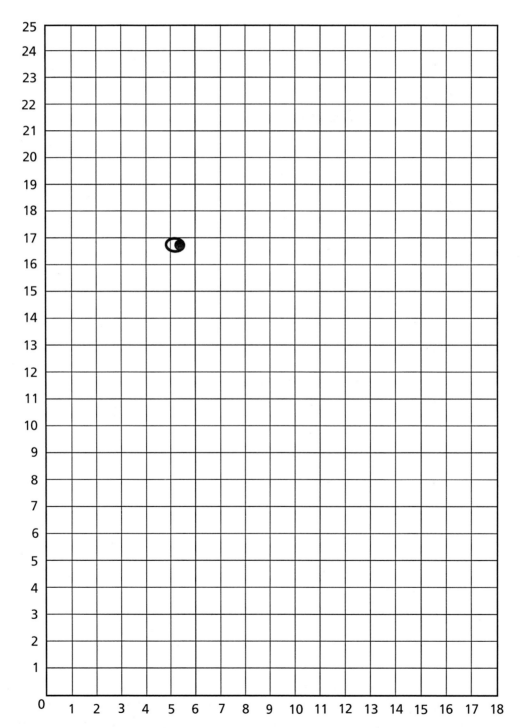

Activity 11

Maths topic: **Addition and subtraction**
Axis: **y only**

Maths co-ordinates

In each pair of brackets below, you have been given the first co-ordinate (on the *x* axis) that will help you to draw a mystery animal on a square grid. But to draw the animal properly, you will need to find the second co-ordinate (on the *y* axis) by working out the answer to the maths question. Write the answer on the blank line inside the pair of brackets.

	Co-ordinates		**Co-ordinates**
$200 - 195 =$ ___	1. (7, ___)	$4 + (9 + 8) =$ ___	19. (10, ___)
$(8 + 6) - 10 =$ ___	2. (5, ___)	Take 7 from 26.	20. (14, ___)
$52 - 49 =$ ___	3. (2, ___)	9 more than 7 is ...	21. (14, ___)
$15 - (6 + 5) =$ ___	4. (3, ___)	10 less than 25 is ...	22. (12, ___)
Take 5 from 9.	5. (1, ___)	$(25 - 10) - 2 =$ ___	23. (13, ___)
9 less than 14 is ...	6. (2, ___)	$4000 - 3990 =$ ___	24. (13, ___)
$(5 + 8) - 7 =$ ___	7. (1, ___)	Double 6.	25. (15, ___)
$21 - (9 + 6) =$ ___	8. (4, ___)	9 more than 3 is ...	26. (16, ___)
Take 7 from 15.	9. (2, ___)	Take 590 from 600.	27. (17, ___)
$3400 - 3390 =$ ___	10. (1, ___)	$(9 + 7) - 8 =$ ___	28. (16, ___)
The sum of 9 and 3 is ...	11. (2, ___)	$300 - 294 =$ ___	29. (14, ___)
$3 + 6 + 3 =$ ___	12. (3, ___)	$(9 + 3) - 6 =$ ___	30. (17, ___)
12 less than 22 is ...	13. (5, ___)	Take 195 from 200.	31. (16, ___)
7 more than 6 is ...	14. (5, ___)	$67 - 63 =$ ___	32. (17, ___)
$6 + 4 + 5 =$ ___	15. (6, ___)	$(8 + 6) - 10 =$ ___	33. (15, ___)
$(8 + 7) + 1 =$ ___	16. (4, ___)	397 less than 400 is ...	34. (16, ___)
$6 + 8 + 5 =$ ___	17. (4, ___)	$98 - 94 =$ ___	35. (13, ___)
The sum of 14 and 7 is ...	18. (8, ___)	$2300 - 2295 =$ ___	36. (11, ___)

CONTINUED ON THE FOLLOWING PAGE

CONTINUED FROM THE PREVIOUS PAGE

Co-ordinates		Co-ordinates

5000 – 4990 = __   37. (6, ____)

Triple 3.   38. (6, ____)

(10 + 9) – 13 = __   39. (7, ____)

Take 8 from 13.   40. (8, ____)

6700 – 6698 = __   41. (6, ____)

92 – 89 = __   42. (7, ____)

70 – 68 = __   43. (7, ____)

(3 + 8) – 8 = __   44. (8, ____)

498 less than 500 is …   45. (8, ____)

(9 + 6) – 11 = __   46. (9, ____)

Take 8 from 17.   47. (9, ____)

8 less than 12 is …   48. (9, ____)

4700 – 4698 = __   49. (10, ____)

(7 + 6) – 10 = __   50. (10, ____)

2000 – 1998 = __   51. (11, ____)

530 – 527 = __   52. (11, ____)

201 – 199 = __   53. (12, ____)

58 less than 63 is …   54. (10, ____)

Take 394 from 400.   55. (11, ____)

(12 + 7) – 10 = __   56. (12, ____)

890 less than 900 is …   57. (12, ____)

7000 – 6980 = __   58. (5, ____)

Triple 7.   59. (5, ____)

(30 – 20) + 12 = __   60. (6, ____)

8 less than 29 is …   61. (7, ____)

(Double 8) + 5 = __   62. (11, ____)

Add 16 to 6.   63. (12, ____)

8 + 5 + 8 = __   64. (13, ____)

6400 – 6380 = __   65. (13, ____)

(25 – 8) + 2 = __   66. (6, ____)

(4 + 8) + 5 = __   67. (7, ____)

(9 + 8) – 1 = __   68. (8, ____)

The sum of 7 and 9 is …   69. (10, ____)

The sum of 12 and 5 is … 70. (11, ____)

11 less than 30 is …   71. (12, ____)

2 + (12 – 8) = __   72. (7, _)

Take 295 from 300.   73. (7, ____)

14 – (5 + 3) = __   74. (11, ____)

(8 + 9) – 12 = __   75. (11, ____)

IMPORTANT NOTE:
Ask your teacher to check your answers before you use these co-ordinates to draw the animal on the next page. All your answers must be correct *before* you draw the animal.

Co-ordinate drawing

Draw a mystery animal using the co-ordinates that you have created by answering the maths questions. Follow these steps to plot the co-ordinates:

1. For each set of co-ordinates, look along the horizontal line to find the first number in the brackets.

2. Look along the vertical line to find the second number in the brackets.

3. Draw a dot on the point where the two gridlines from these numbers meet.

4. Join one dot to the next by ruling a line.

5. Start to draw a new line each time you get to some waves ~~~~~~.

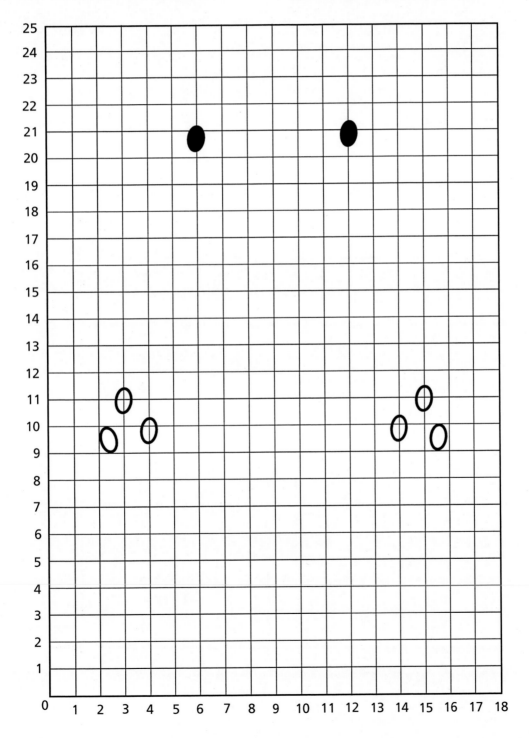

© Essential Resources Educational Publishers Ltd, 2008

Activity 12

Maths topic: **Multiplication tables**
Axis: **x and y**

Maths co-ordinates

In each pair of brackets below, you will make the two co-ordinates that you need to draw a mystery animal on a square grid. Find the co-ordinates by working out the answers to the pair of multiplication tables. Write the two answers on the two lines inside the brackets (with the first answer on the first line and the second answer on the second line).

		Co-ordinates			**Co-ordinates**
7 × 1 = __	1 × 13 = __	1. (__, __)	1 × 17 = __	3 × 2 = __	28. (__, __)
2 × 4 = __	3 × 4 = __	2. (__, __)	8 × 2 = __	5 × 1 = __	29. (__, __)
3 × 3 = __	6 × 2 = __	3. (__, __)	3 × 4 = __	1 × 5 = __	30. (__, __)
2 × 5 = __	13 × 1 = __	4. (__, __)	5 × 2 = __	3 × 2 = __	31. (__, __)
2 × 6 = __	7 × 2 = __	5. (__, __)	3 × 3 = __	1 × 7 = __	32. (__, __)
4 × 4 = __	2 × 7 = __	6. (__, __)	7 × 1 = __	1 × 7 = __	33. (__, __)
1 × 17 = __	5 × 3 = __	7. (__, __)	3 × 2 = __	6 × 1 = __	34. (__, __)
17 × 1 = __	8 × 2 = __	8. (__, __)	3 × 3 = __	7 × 1 = __	35. (__, __)
4 × 4 = __	3 × 5 = __	9. (__, __)	5 × 2 = __	10 × 1 = __	36. (__, __)
3 × 3 = __	5 × 3 = __	10. (__, __)	1 × 10 = __	13 × 1 = __	37. (__, __)
5 × 1 = __	6 × 3 = __	11. (__, __)	2 × 7 = __	13 × 1 = __	38. (__, __)
2 × 3 = __	10 × 2 = __	12. (__, __)	5 × 3 = __	7 × 2 = __	39. (__, __)
7 × 1 = __	7 × 3 = __	13. (__, __)	10 × 1 = __	2 × 3 = __	40. (__, __)
1 × 7 = __	11 × 2 = __	14. (__, __)	3 × 5 = __	3 × 2 = __	41. (__, __)
3 × 2 = __	2 × 11 = __	15. (__, __)	4 × 4 = __	7 × 1 = __	42. (__, __)
2 × 2 = __	3 × 7 = __	16. (__, __)	8 × 2 = __	3 × 2 = __	43. (__, __)
1 × 2 = __	19 × 1 = __	17. (__, __)	5 × 3 = __	5 × 1 = __	44. (__, __)
3 × 1 = __	8 × 2 = __	18. (__, __)	1 × 5 = __	2 × 2 = __	45. (__, __)
1 × 5 = __	2 × 5 = __	19. (__, __)	3 × 2 = __	2 × 1 = __	46. (__, __)
2 × 2 = __	1 × 7 = __	20. (__, __)	2 × 5 = __	1 × 2 = __	47. (__, __)
5 × 1 = __	4 × 1 = __	21. (__, __)	13 × 1 = __	3 × 1 = __	48. (__, __)
3 × 2 = __	1 × 3 = __	22. (__, __)	2 × 3 = __	1 × 3 = __	49. (__, __)
3 × 3 = __	2 × 2 = __	23. (__, __)	2 × 1 = __	6 × 3 = __	50. (__, __)
5 × 2 = __	5 × 1 = __	24. (__, __)	1 × 1 = __	19 × 1 = __	51. (__, __)
3 × 4 = __	2 × 2 = __	25. (__, __)	2 × 1 = __	1 × 19 = __	52. (__, __)
4 × 4 = __	4 × 1 = __	26. (__, __)	1 × 1 = __	4 × 5 = __	53. (__, __)
17 × 1 = __	5 × 1 = __	27. (__, __)	2 × 1 = __	10 × 2 = __	54. (__, __)

IMPORTANT NOTE:
Ask your teacher to check your answers before you use these co-ordinates to draw the animal on the next page. All your answers must be correct *before* you draw the animal.

Co-ordinate drawing

Draw a mystery animal using the co-ordinates that you have created by answering the maths questions. Follow these steps to plot the co-ordinates:

1. For each set of co-ordinates, look along the horizontal line to find the first number in the brackets.

2. Look along the vertical line to find the second number in the brackets.

3. Draw a dot on the point where the two gridlines from these numbers meet.

4. Join one dot to the next by ruling a line.

5. Start to draw a new line each time you get to some waves ~~~~~.

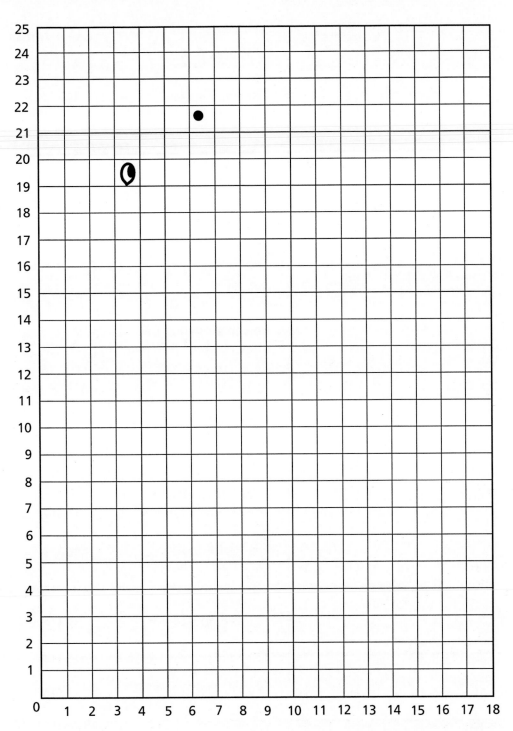

Activity 13

Drawing level: **MEDIUM**

Maths topic: **Mixed maths**
Axis: **y only**

Maths co-ordinates

In each pair of brackets below, you have been given the first co-ordinate (on the *x* axis) that will help you to draw a mystery animal on a square grid. But to draw the animal properly, you will need to find the second co-ordinate (on the *y* axis) by working out the answer to the maths question. Write the answer on the blank line inside the pair of brackets.

	Co-ordinates		**Co-ordinates**
(6 × 3) – 5 = __	1. (9, ____)	Multiply 7 by 2.	19. (13, ____)
Half of 28 is …	2. (8, ____)	130 mm = __ cm	20. (12, ____)
4 squared is …	3. (7, ____)	How many minutes are there between 8:27 and 8:40?	21. (9, ____)
$(3^2) + 8 =$ __	4. (6, ____)	$^1/_2$ of 42	22. (7, ____)
(7 × 4) – 9 = __	5. (5, ____)	3400 – 3380 = __	23. (8, ____)
Multiply 7 by 3.	6. (5, ____)	20.8 – 1.8 = __	24. (8, ____)
The sum of 13 and 9 is …	7. (6, ____)	Triple 6.	25. (7, ____)
The product of 11 and 2 is …	8. (8, ____)	How many minutes are there between 5:50 and 6:09?	26. (6, ____)
(3 × 3) + (4 × 3) = __	9. (9, ____)	$^1/_5$ of 100 is …	27. (6, ____)
One quarter of 88 is …	10. (10, ____)	7 more than 14 is …	28. (7, ____)
54 – __ = 32	11. (11, ____)	__ days = 3 weeks	29. (14, ____)
The product of 7 and 3 is …	12. (12, ____)	How many years are there in 2 decades?	30. (15, ____)
The second multiple of 11 is …	13. (13, ____)	3 + 7 + 9 = __	31. (15, ____)
Double 11.	14. (15, ____)	2)36	32. (14, ____)
(Double 8) + 5 = __	15. (16, ____)	11 less than 30 is …	33. (13, ____)
(25 – 8) + 2 = __	16. (16, ____)	800 – 780 = __	34. (13, ____)
How many minutes are there between 11:09 and 11:26?	17. (15, ____)	(2 × 7) + (7 × 1) = __	35. (14, ____)
9 more than 7 is …	18. (14, ____)		

CONTINUED ON THE FOLLOWING PAGE

CONTINUED FROM THE PREVIOUS PAGE

Co-ordinates ———————— **Co-ordinates**

$(4 \times 5) - 5 =$ ___	36. (9, ____)	How many minutes are there between 7:57 and 8:06?	58. (12, ____)
140 mm = ___ cm	37. (10, ____)	___ l = 8000 ml	59. (12, ____)
A fortnight = ___ days	38. (11, ____)	Subtract 10 from 23.	60. (9, ____)
The product of 5 and 3 is ...	39. (12, ____)	Which is prime: 12 or 13?	61. (5, ____)
8 more than 6 is ...	40. (13, ____)	How many hours are there in half a day?	62. (4, ____)
$130 \div 10 =$ ___	41. (14, ____)	$99 \div 9 =$ ___	63. (5, ____)
Which is prime: 10 or 11?	42. (15, ____)	$\frac{1}{4}$ of 44	64. (6, ____)
$3\overline{)24}$	43. (16, ____)	Take 590 from 600.	65. (9, ____)
$700 \div 100 =$ ___	44. (16, ____)	___ months = 2 years	66. (2, ____)
5000 g = ___ kg	45. (15, ____)	Divide 39 by 3.	67. (5, ____)
$\frac{1}{3}$ of 12 is ...	46. (13, ____)	The third multiple of 8 is ...	68. (1, ____)
$7\overline{)28}$	47. (11, ____)	$4.7 + 8.3 =$ ___	69. (4, ____)
Divide 40 by 8.	48. (9, ____)	$\frac{1}{3}$ of 33 minutes is ___ minutes.	70. (5, ____)
500 cm = ___ m	49. (7, ____)	Triple 3.	71. (6, ____)
$400 - 394 =$ ___	50. (6, ____)	$8.3 + 2.7 =$ ___	72. (6, ____)
$\frac{2}{3}$ of 12 months is ___ months.	51. (5, ____)	$\frac{3}{4}$ of 12 months is ___ months.	73. (7, ____)
3 squared is ...	52. (6, ____)	The square root of 25 is ...	74. (8, ____)
___ cm = 90 mm	53. (7, ____)	$400 - 398 =$ ___	75. (9, ____)
The quotient of 24 and 3 is ...	54. (8, ____)	Take 295 from 300.	76. (9, ____)
$3\overline{)27}$	55. (8, ____)	Divide 20 by 10.	77. (10, ____)
$50 \times$ ___ = 500	56. (9, ____)		
$1400 - 1390 =$ ___	57. (10, ____)		

IMPORTANT NOTE:
Ask your teacher to check your answers before you use these co-ordinates to draw the animal on the next page. All your answers must be correct *before* you draw the animal.

Co-ordinate drawing

Draw a mystery animal using the co-ordinates that you have created by answering the maths questions. Follow these steps to plot the co-ordinates:

1. For each set of co-ordinates, look along the horizontal line to find the first number in the brackets.

2. Look along the vertical line to find the second number in the brackets.

3. Draw a dot on the point where the two gridlines from these numbers meet.

4. Join one dot to the next by ruling a line.

5. Start to draw a new line each time you get to some waves ~~~~~.

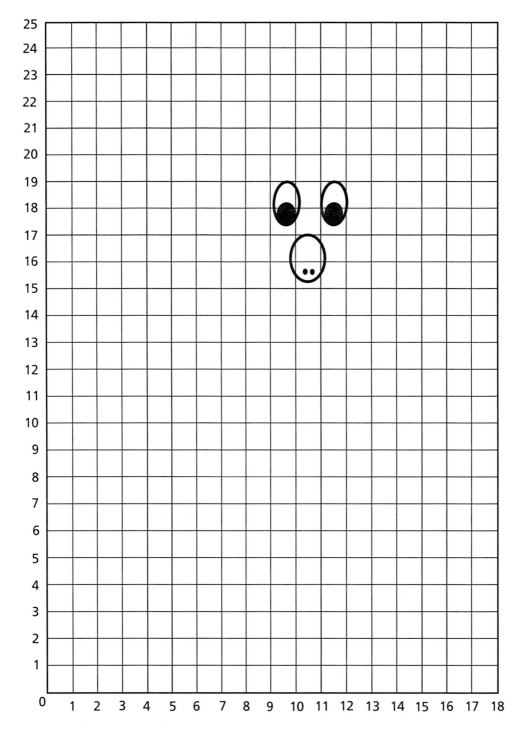

Activity 14

Maths topic: **Division**
Axis: *x only*

Maths co-ordinates

In each pair of brackets below, you have been given the second co-ordinate (on the *y* axis) that will help you to draw a mystery animal on a square grid. But to draw the animal properly, you will need to find the first co-ordinate (on the *x* axis) by working out the answer to the maths question. Write the answer on the blank line inside the pair of brackets.

	Co-ordinates		**Co-ordinates**
6)24	1. (____, 4)	Divide 39 by 3.	19. (____, 22)
25 ÷ 5 = __	2. (____, 3)	2)28	20. (____, 22)
Divide 30 by 6.	3. (____, 1)	The quotient of 30 and 2 is …	21. (____, 21)
The quotient of 16 and 4 is …	4. (____, 0)	1400 ÷ 100 = __	22. (____, 19)
6 ÷ 6 = __	5. (____, 0)	3)36	23. (____, 18)
7)14	6. (____, 1)	4)36	24. (____, 18)
20 ÷ 10 = __	7. (____, 3)	The quotient of 24 and 3 is …	25. (____, 17)
8)8	8. (____, 4)	110 ÷ 10 = __	26. (____, 17)
9)18	9. (____, 4)	Divide 28 by 2.	27. (____, 18)
Divide 15 by 5.	10. (____, 5)	160 ÷ 10 = __	28. (____, 17)
5)20	11. (____, 7)	Divide 32 by 2.	29. (____, 16)
55 ÷ 11 = __	12. (____, 15)	140 ÷ 10 = __	30. (____, 17)
600 ÷ 100 = __	13. (____, 17)	2)24	31. (____, 15)
3)21	14. (____, 18)	4)36	32. (____, 16)
The quotient of 27 and 3 is …	15. (____, 19)	44 ÷ 4 = __	33. (____, 15)
130 ÷ 10 = __	16. (____, 19)	Divide 30 by 2.	34. (____, 15)
14,000 ÷ 1000 = __	17. (____, 20)	2)34	35. (____, 14)
Divide 28 by 2.	18. (____, 21)	1700 ÷ 100 = __	36. (____, 13)

CONTINUED ON THE FOLLOWING PAGE

CONTINUED FROM THE PREVIOUS PAGE

Co-ordinates ——— ——— Co-ordinates

$2\overline{)30}$	37. (____, 14)
$13 \div 1 =$ __	38. (____, 13)
The quotient of 40 and 4 is ...	39. (____, 12)
$3\overline{)24}$	40. (____, 12)
$88 \div 8 =$ __	41. (____, 12)
$4\overline{)40}$	42. (____, 7)
The quotient of 30 and 2 is ...	43. (____, 7)
$1600 \div 100 =$ __	44. (____, 6)
$16 \div 1 =$ __	45. (____, 4)
$1500 \div 100 =$ __	46. (____, 5)
$2\overline{)26}$	47. (____, 5)
Divide 18 by 2.	48. (____, 4)
$77 \div 11 =$ __	49. (____, 3)
$5\overline{)25}$	50. (____, 3)
$90 \div 10 =$ __	51. (____, 7)
$1300 \div 100 =$ __	52. (____, 6)
Divide 60 by 4.	53. (____, 6)
$2\overline{)32}$	54. (____, 5)
Divide 24 by 6.	55. (____, 5)
$3\overline{)15}$	56. (____, 5)

$7 \div 1 =$ __	57. (____, 4)
$55 \div 11 =$ __	58. (____, 6)
The quotient of 45 and 5 is ...	59. (____, 5)
Divide 40 by 8.	60. (____, 8)
$77 \div 11 =$ __	61. (____, 7)
$6\overline{)30}$	62. (____, 10)
$90 \div 10 =$ __	63. (____, 9)
$500 \div 100 =$ __	64. (____, 12)
$4\overline{)28}$	65. (____, 11)
The quotient of 60 and 6 is ...	66. (____, 10)
$6\overline{)36}$	67. (____, 14)
$900 \div 100 =$ __	68. (____, 14)
$11 \div 1 =$ __	69. (____, 13)
Divide 30 by 5.	70. (____, 16)
$88 \div 11 =$ __	71. (____, 16)
The quotient of 90 and 10 is ...	72. (____, 15)
$1\overline{)9}$	73. (____, 19)
$100 \div 10 =$ __	74. (____, 18)
$66 \div 6 =$ __	75. (____, 19)
$4\overline{)48}$	76. (____, 18)

IMPORTANT NOTE:
Ask your teacher to check your answers before you use these co-ordinates to draw the animal on the next page. All your answers must be correct *before* you draw the animal.

Co-ordinate drawing

Draw a mystery animal using the co-ordinates that you have created by answering the maths questions. Follow these steps to plot the co-ordinates:

1. For each set of co-ordinates, look along the horizontal line to find the first number in the brackets.

2. Look along the vertical line to find the second number in the brackets.

3. Draw a dot on the point where the two gridlines from these numbers meet.

4. Join one dot to the next by ruling a line.

5. Start to draw a new line each time you get to some waves ~~~~~~.

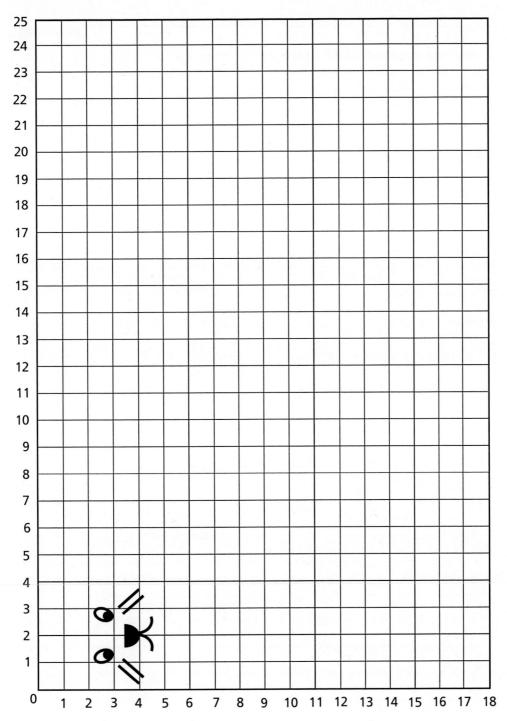

Activity 15

Maths topic: **Mixed maths**
Axis: **x or y**

Maths co-ordinates

In each pair of brackets below, you have been given one co-ordinate that will help you to draw a mystery animal on a square grid. But to draw the animal properly, you will need to find the other co-ordinate by working out the answer to the maths question. Write the answer on the blank line inside the pair of brackets.

Co-ordinates

How many minutes are there between 3:23 and 3:30?.......................................	1. (____, 16)
$(2 \times 3) + (4 \times 3) =$ ___	2. (7, ____)
$(3 \times 5) + 4 =$ ___	3. (8, ____)
Divide 18 by 2.	4. (____, 19)
$700 - 690 =$ ___	5. (____, 18)
4 squared is …	6. (10, ____)
$2.5 + 4.5 =$ ___	7. (____, 16)
$4\overline{)24}$	8. (____, 15)
2 lots of 7 is …	9. (6, ____)
How many days are there in a week?	10. (____, 13)
$(4 \times 5) - 7 =$ ___	11. (10, ____)
___ days = 1 fortnight	12. (11, ____)
The product of 5 and 3 is …	13. (11, ____)
$3400 - 3390 =$ ___	14. (____, 16)
$700 \div 100 =$ ___	15. (____, 13)
Which is composite: 6 or 7?	16. (____, 11)
The square root of 36 is …	17. (6, ____)
How many hours are there between 8:00 am and 12 noon?	18. (8, ____)
$3.4 + 4.6 =$ ___	19. (____, 2)
3 squared is …	20. (____, 2)
$^{1}/_{3}$ of 12 is …...	21. (9, ____)
$6000 \div 1000 =$ ___	22. (11, ____)
One quarter of 44 is …	23. (____, 11)
How many minutes are there between 8:53 and 9:03?	24. (____, 13)
The second multiple of 8 is …	25. (7, ____)
$2000 \ g =$ ___ kg	26. (____, 20)
$^{1}/_{5}$ of 100 is	27. (0, ____)
Quarter of an hour = ___ minutes	28. (0, ____)
Which is prime: 7 or 8?	29. (____, 13)
The quotient of 18 and 3 is	30. (____, 15)
Half of 36 is …	31. (0, ____)
$4000 - 3990 =$ ___	32. (____, 16)
Multiply 4 by 5.	33. (16, ____)
How many years are there in 2 decades?	34. (18, ____)
The sum of 7 and 11 is	35. (____, 15)
$(5 \times 5) - 12 =$ ___	36. (10, ____)
$33 \div 3 =$ ___	37. (____, 15)
From 24 take 6.	38. (18, ____)

CONTINUED ON THE FOLLOWING PAGE

42

CONTINUED ON THE FOLLOWING PAGE

Co-ordinates

70 mm = __ cm	39. (____, 16)
Triple 6.	40. (6, ____)
__ months = half a year	41. (____, 19)
__ years = 1 decade	42. (____, 16)
29 subtract 11 equals	43. (11, ____)
26 minus 7 equals …	44. (11, ____)
(6 × 2) + 7 = __	45. (8, ____)
The fourth multiple of 5 is …	46. (7, ____)
2)14	47. (____, 21)
4.5 + 4.5 = __	48. (____, 19)
800 – 790 = __	49. (____, 20)
Multiply 7 by 3.	50. (10, ____)
The quotient of 21 and 3 is …	51. (____, 13)
300 cm = __ m	52. (____, 11)
6000 – 5990 = __	53. (3, ____)
55 ÷ 5 = __	54. (6, ____)
How many hours are there between 3:00 pm and 7:00 pm?	55. (____, 7)
40 mm = __ cm	56. (____, 6)
How many minutes are there between 5:30 and 5:40?	57. (____, 13)
The product of 2 and 7 is …	58. (____, 11)
The square root of 100 is …	59. (14, ____)
Which is prime: 10 or 11?	60. (11, ____)
How many minutes are there between 7:16 and 7:29?	61. (____, 7)
600 ÷ 100 = __	62. (13, ____)
¼ of 20 is …	63. (7, ____)
Divide 25 by 5.	64. (10, ____)
Subtract 18 from 24.	65. (____, 6)
How many hours are there between 9:00 am and 3:00 pm?	66. (11, ____)
$^2/_3$ of 12 is …	67. (6, ____)
800 ÷ 100 = __	68. (11, ____)
3)18	69. (____, 9)
10.3 – 1.3 = __	70. (11, ____)
6000 ml = __ L	71. (____, 11)
7.5 + 3.5 = __	72. (11, ____)
3 lots of 4 is …	73. (7, ____)
120 ÷ 10 = __	74. (10, ____)
(3^2) + 8 = __	75. (7, ____)
$^1/_5$ of 40 is …	76. (____, 17)
Take 7 from 26.	77. (8, ____)
(4 squared) – 6 = __	78. (____, 17)
How many minutes are there between 5:36 and 5:45?	79. (____, 17)
(7 × 4) – 9 = __	80. (9, ____)

IMPORTANT NOTE:
Ask your teacher to check your answers before you use these co-ordinates to draw the
animal on the next page. All your answers must be correct *before* you draw the animal.

Co-ordinate drawing

Draw a mystery animal using the co-ordinates that you have created by answering the maths questions. Follow these steps to plot the co-ordinates:

1. For each set of co-ordinates, look along the horizontal line to find the first number in the brackets.

2. Look along the vertical line to find the second number in the brackets.

3. Draw a dot on the point where the two gridlines from these numbers meet.

4. Join one dot to the next by ruling a line.

5. Start to draw a new line each time you get to some waves ~~~~~~.

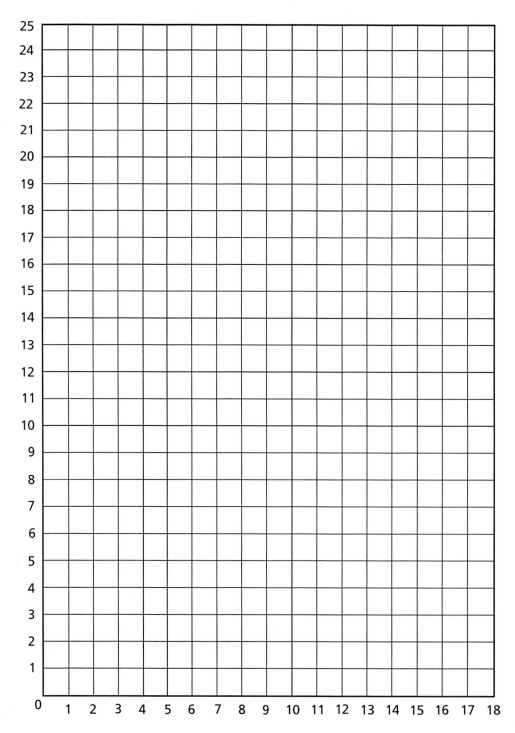

Activity 16

Maths topic: **Mixed maths**
Axis: **x or y**

Maths co-ordinates

In each pair of brackets below, you have been given one co-ordinate that will help you to draw a mystery animal on a square grid. But to draw the animal properly, you will need to find the other co-ordinate by working out the answer to the maths question. Write the answer on the blank line inside the pair of brackets.

	Co-ordinates
$3.4 + 3.6 =$ ___	1. (___, 18)
$500 \div$ ___ $= 50$	2. (___, 14)
$3\overline{)18}$	3. (10, ___)
How many minutes are there between 7:38 and 7:47?	4. (___, 5)
$(3 \times 5) - 7 =$ ___	5. (___, 6)
$32 \div 4 =$ ___	6. (___, 14)
The sum of 6 and 12 is …	7. (11, ___)
___ $\times 10 = 80$	8. (___, 14)
Triple 6.	9. (4, ___)
$5 \div 5 =$ ___	10. (___, 18)
The fourth multiple of 4 is …	11. (1, ___)
Divide 20 by 10.	12. (___, 12)
Take 28 from 32.	13. (___, 10)
$(8 \times 3) - 13 =$ ___	14. (8, ___)
$3000 - 2990 =$ ___	15. (4, ___)
48 hours = ___ days	16. (___, 8)
$\frac{1}{4}$ of 20 is …	17. (1, ___)
How many hours are there between 6:00 am and 9:00 am?	18. (4, ___)
300 cm = ___ m	19. (6, ___)
$3.4 + 4.6 =$ ___	20. (___, 6)

	Co-ordinates
How many days are there in a fortnight?	21. (10, ___)
$180 \div 10 =$ ___	22. (14, ___)
$(6 \times 4) - 7 =$ ___	23. (___, 18)
How many minutes are there between 2:15 and 2:32?	24. (___, 16)
How many months are there in a year?	25. (16, ___)
$5600 - 5590 =$ ___	26. (14, ___)
$55 \div 5 =$ ___	27. (10, ___)
$4200 - 4190 =$ ___	28. (14, ___)
4 squared = ___	29. (___, 8)
Which is prime: 5 or 8?	30. (17, ___)
$(15 \div 3) + 9 =$ ___	31. (___, 3)
$\frac{1}{3}$ of 36 is …	32. (___, 3)
The fifth multiple of 2 is …	33. (___, 6)
$7.8 - 4.8 =$ ___	34. (___, 16)
3000 ml = ___ l	35. (___, 15)
Which is composite: 11 or 12?	36. (4, ___)
How many days are there in 1 week?	37. (___, 12)
The product of 7 and 2 is …	38. (7, ___)
One fifth of 25 is …	39. (___, 16)

CONTINUED ON THE FOLLOWING PAGE

CONTINUED FROM THE PREVIOUS PAGE

Co-ordinates		Co-ordinates

Double 8.	40. (3, ___)	Triple 4.	63. (11, ___)
4)16̄	41. (___, 15)	(5 × 4) – 8 = ___	64. (14, ___)
19 minus 6 equals …	42. (5, ___)	150 ÷ 10 = ___	65. (___, 15)
Subtract 8 from 21.	43. (6, ___)	How many minutes are there between 8:45 and 9:00?	66. (___, 16)
Halve 28.	44. (6, ___)	48 – ___ = 34	67. (___, 15)
½ of 30 is …	45. (5, ___)	500 – 485 = ___	68. (13, ___)
400 ÷ 100 = ___	46. (___, 15)	(4 × 5) – 6 = ___	69. (12, ___)
4)28̄	47. (___, 9)	3 × ___ = 36	70. (___, 13)
5000 g = ___ kg	48. (___, 9)	28 – (8 + 7) = ___	71. (13, ___)
6.7 – 3.7 = ___	49. (___, 8)	5400 – 5385 = ___	72. (14, ___)
How many hours are there between 6:30 and 11:30?	50. (3, ___)	$\frac{1}{4}$ of 36 is …	73. (11, ___)
(8 × 3) – 19 = ___	51. (5, ___)	Divide 14 by 2.	74. (11, ___)
2.6 + 4.4 = ___	52. (___, 7)	500 cm = ___ m	75. (13, ___)
Which is composite: 7 or 9?	53. (7, ___)	(20 ÷ 2) – (15 ÷ 3) = ___	76. (15, ___)
The square root of 64 is …	54. (6, ___)	800 – 785 = ___	77. (___, 8)
5)25̄	55. (___, 8)	2)18̄	78. (13, ___)
4000 ml = ___ l	56. (___, 7)	The third multiple of 3 is …	79. (11, ___)
One third of 12 is …	57. (___, 6)	The product of 3 and 4 is …	80. (___, 8)
How many minutes are there between 5:28 and 5:34?	58. (5, ___)	2000 – 1994 = ___	81. (13, ___)
___ months = half a year	59. (___, 8)	How many minutes are there between 6:58 and 7:12?	82. (___, 6)
The sum of 7 and 9 is …	60. (15, ___)	Which is prime: 7 or 8?	83. (14, ___)
Halve 32.	61. (13, ___)	2)16̄	84. (13, ___)
33 ÷ 3 = ___	62. (___, 14)	$\frac{2}{3}$ of 12 is …	85. (12, ___)

IMPORTANT NOTE:
Ask your teacher to check your answers before you use these co-ordinates to draw the animal on the next page. All your answers must be correct *before* you draw the animal.

Co-ordinate drawing

Draw a mystery animal using the co-ordinates that you have created by answering the maths questions. Follow these steps to plot the co-ordinates:

1. For each set of co-ordinates, look along the horizontal line to find the first number in the brackets.

2. Look along the vertical line to find the second number in the brackets.

3. Draw a dot on the point where the two gridlines from these numbers meet.

4. Join one dot to the next by ruling a line.

5. Start to draw a new line each time you get to some waves ~~~~~~.

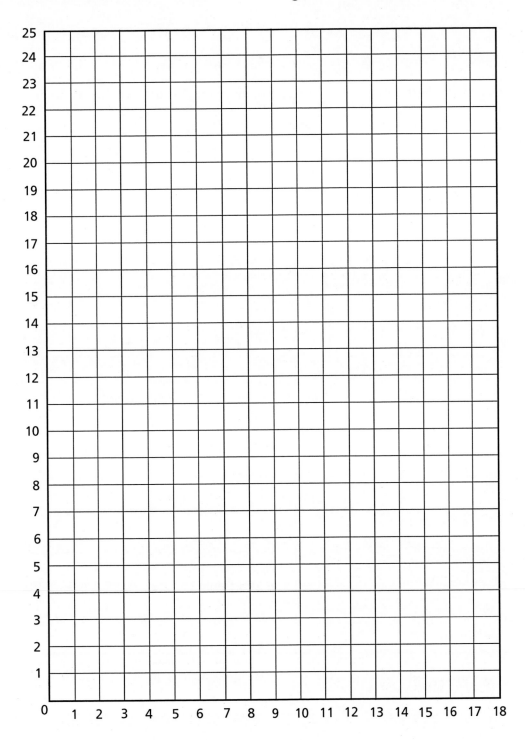

Activity 17

Drawing level: **HARD**

Maths topic: **Mixed maths**
Axis: **x or y**

Maths co-ordinates

In each pair of brackets below, you have been given one co-ordinate that will help you to draw a mystery animal on a square grid. But to draw the animal properly, you will need to find the other co-ordinate by working out the answer to the maths question. Write the answer on the blank line inside the pair of brackets.

	Co-ordinates		**Co-ordinates**
Take 7 from 26.	1. (8, ___)	2.5 + 4.5 = __	20. (___, 21)
How many months are there in half a year?	2. (___, 17)	The third multiple of 7 is ...	21. (6, ___)
How many minutes are there in quarter of an hour?	3. (5, ___)	3000 – 2990 = __	22. (___, 19)
30 mm = __ cm	4. (___, 13)	(3 × 3) + (4 × 3) = __	23. (11, ___)
33 ÷ 3 = __	5. (2, ___)	The product of 7 and 3 is ...	24. (12, ___)
2.5 + 2.5 = __	6. (2, ___)	3000 g = __ kg	25. (___, 19)
Which is prime: 3 or 6?	7. (3, ___)	The sum of 7 and 11 is ...	26. (3, ___)
$\frac{1}{4}$ of 20 is ...	8. (___, 1)	Halve 30.	27. (5, ___)
__ days = 1 week	9. (___, 0)	(6 × 4) – 9 = __	28. (13, ___)
0 ÷ 5 = __	10. (11, ___)	150 ÷ 10 = __	29. (___, 18)
(6 × 3) – 5 = __	11. (___, 1)	3 + 7 + 9 = __	30. (15, ___)
How many hours are there between 4 am and 7 am?	12. (15, ___)	How many minutes are there between 2:15 and 2:30?	31. (9, ___)
The sum of 9 and 7 is ...	13. (___, 5)	3 squared is ...	32. (___, 0)
26 subtract 10 equals ...	14. (___, 11)	$\frac{1}{3}$ of 12 is ...	33. (___, 14)
Triple 5.	15. (___, 13)	0 ÷ 10 = __	34. (___, 11)
The product of 5 and 3 is ...	16. (13, ___)	2500 – 2490 = __	35. (0, ___)
$(3^2) + 8 = __$	17. (12, ___)	How many days are there in a fortnight?	36. (___, 14)
How many years are there in a decade?	18. (___, 19)	55 ÷ 5 = __	37. (18, ___)
Which is composite: 7 or 8?	19. (___, 19)	Multiply 6 by 3.	38. (___, 10)
		__ decades = 50 years	39. (2, ___)

CONTINUED ON THE FOLLOWING PAGE

Activity 17

CONTINUED FROM THE PREVIOUS PAGE

	Co-ordinates		**Co-ordinates**
2000 g = __ kg	40. (0, ____)	Divide 21 by 3.	62. (12, ____)
6 ÷ 6 = __	41. (0, ____)	2 weeks = __ days	63. (____, 9)
4 squared is …	42. (____, 5)	How many minutes are there between 12:46 and 12:57?	64. (12, ____)
Halve 36.	43. (____, 2)	3.6 + 3.4 = __	65. (4, ____)
Triple 6.	44. (____, 1)	5400 − 5394 = __	66. (3, ____)
$^2/_3$ of 9 is …	45. (____, 14)	The square root of 25 is …	67. (4, ____)
28 − (8 + 7) = __	46. (5, ____)	(8 × 3) − 19 = __	68. (____, 6)
How many minutes are there between 6:29 and 6:35?	47. (____, 12)	$(4^2) − 9 = $__	69. (4, ____)
4)‾28	48. (____, 13)	32 minus 25 equals …	70. (____, 4)
9.3 + 4.7 = __	49. (6, ____)	(4 × 3) ÷ (2 × 2) = __	71. (6, ____)
(18 + 6) − 12 = __	50. (____, 14)	1.3 + 0.7 = __	72. (7, ____)
44 ÷ 4 = __	51. (____, 13)	32 ÷ 4 = __	73. (____, 3)
How many months are there in a year?	52. (12, ____)	70 mm = __ cm	74. (____, 4)
Three squared + 4 = __	53. (____, 13)	2000 − 1993 = __	75. (14, ____)
½ of 28 is …	54. (12, ____)	(7 × 3) − 8 = __	76. (____, 6)
Divide 77 by 7.	55. (6, ____)	The product of 2 and 7 is …	77. (____, 5)
__l = 4000 ml	56. (____, 9)	2 + (12 − 8) = __	78. (15, ____)
600 ÷ 100 = __	57. (____, 7)	How many minutes are there between 7:58 and 8:12?	79. (____, 7)
How many hours are there between 10 pm and 6 am?	58. (____, 9)	110 ÷ 10 = __	80. (____, 4)
The quotient of 24 and 4 is …	59. (____, 11)	7700 − 7690 = __	81. (____, 3)
Factors of 11 = 1 and __	60. (12, ____)	200 years = __ centuries	82. (11, ____)
Subtract 8 from 17.	61. (10, ____)	7.8 − 4.8 = __	83. (12, ____)
		One third of 12 is …	84. (11, ____)

! IMPORTANT NOTE:
Ask your teacher to check your answers before you use these co-ordinates to draw the animal on the next page. All your answers must be correct *before* you draw the animal.

© Essential Resources Educational Publishers Ltd, 2008

49

Co-ordinate drawing

Draw a mystery animal using the co-ordinates that you have created by answering the maths questions. Follow these steps to plot the co-ordinates:

1. For each set of co-ordinates, look along the horizontal line to find the first number in the brackets.

2. Look along the vertical line to find the second number in the brackets.

3. Draw a dot on the point where the two gridlines from these numbers meet.

4. Join one dot to the next by ruling a line.

5. Start to draw a new line each time you get to some waves ~~~~~~~.

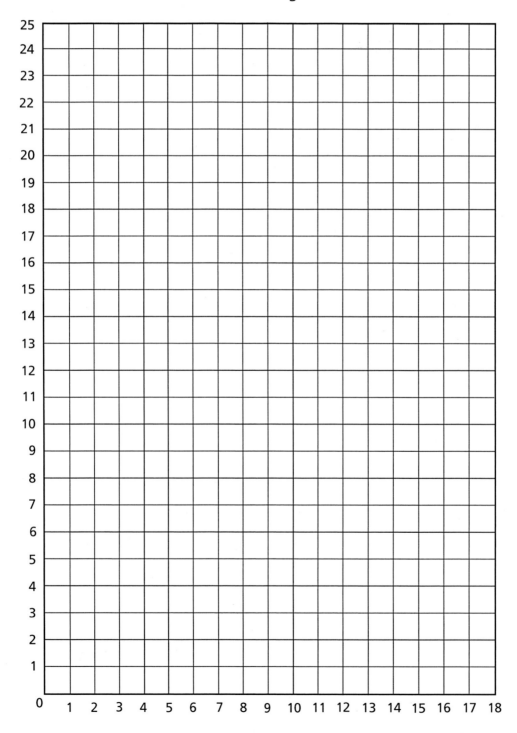

Answers Completed animal drawings

Drawing level: Easy

Drawing level: Medium

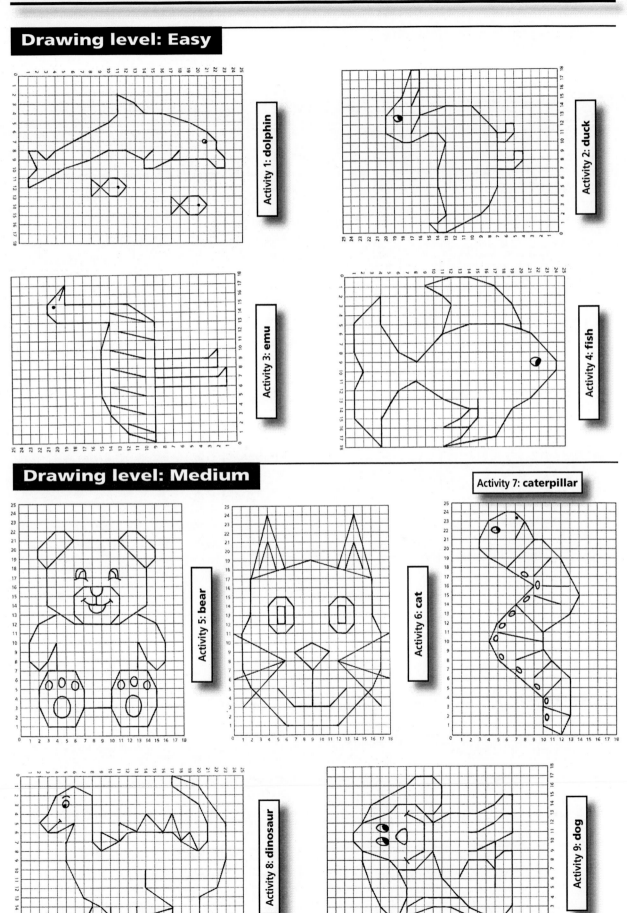

Activity 1: dolphin

Activity 2: duck

Activity 3: emu

Activity 4: fish

Activity 5: bear

Activity 6: cat

Activity 7: caterpillar

Activity 8: dinosaur

Activity 9: dog

Drawing level: Medium

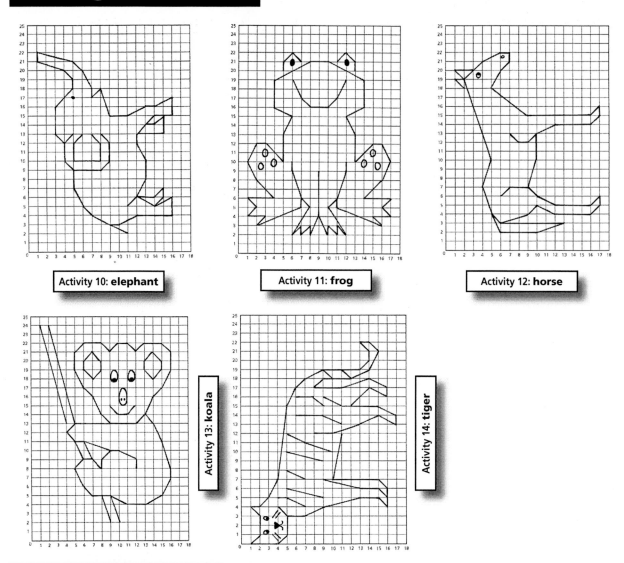

Activity 10: **elephant**

Activity 11: **frog**

Activity 12: **horse**

Activity 13: **koala**

Activity 14: **tiger**

Drawing level: Hard

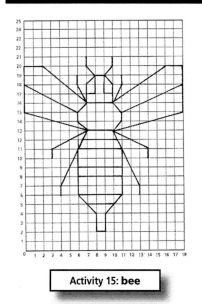

Activity 15: **bee**

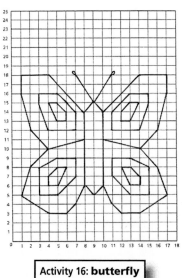

Activity 16: **butterfly**

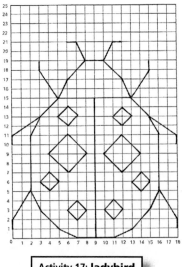

Activity 17: **ladybird**

Answers Completed co-ordinates

Level: Easy	Level: Easy	Level: Easy	Level: Easy	Level: Medium	Level: Medium	Level: Medium
Activity 1 Dolphin	Activity 2 Duck	Activity 3 Emu	Activity 4 Fish	Activity 5 Bear	Activity 5 Bear (cont.)	Activity 6 Cat
1. (9, 17)	1. (11, 17)	1. (0, 9)	1. (13, 15)	1. (6, 21)	54. (3, 7)	1. (9, 19)
2. (9, 21)	2. (13, 16)	2. (13, 9)	2. (15, 15)	2. (3, 18)	55. (2, 5)	2. (2, 17)
3. (10, 22)	3. (18, 16)	3. (15, 12)	3. (17, 13)	3. (3, 14)	56. (2, 3)	3. (2, 13)
4. (10, 23)	4. (18, 17)	4. (15, 19)	4. (18, 11)	4. (6, 12)	57. (3, 1)	4. (1, 11)
5. (9, 23)	5. (15, 18)	5. (17, 19)	5. (17, 17)	5. (11, 12)	58. (6, 1)	5. (1, 7)
6. (8, 22)	6. (13, 20)	6. (15, 21)	6. (14, 19)	6. (14, 14)	59. (7, 3)	6. (2, 5)
7. (7, 22)	7. (11, 20)	7. (14, 21)	7. (13, 21)	7. (14, 18)	60. (7, 5)	7. (6, 1)
8. (6, 21)	8. (10, 18)	8. (13, 20)	8. (10, 24)	8. (11, 21)	61. (6, 7)	8. (12, 1)
9. (5, 19)	9. (10, 17)	9. (13, 14)	9. (9, 24)	9. (6, 21)	62. (3, 7)	9. (16, 5)
10. (4, 16)	10. (11, 15)	10. (10, 15)	10. (6, 21)	10. (5, 22)	63. (7, 3)	10. (17, 7)
11. (4, 14)	11. (11, 14)	11. (5, 15)	11. (5, 18)	11. (4, 22)	64. (10, 3)	11. (17, 11)
12. (3, 13)	12. (10, 13)	12. (3, 14)	12. (5, 14)	12. (2, 20)		12. (16, 13)
13. (2, 11)	13. (7, 14)	13. (1, 12)	13. (6, 11)	13. (2, 19)		13. (16, 17)
14. (4, 11)	14. (5, 14)	14. (0, 9)	14. (9, 8)	14. (3, 18)		14. (12, 18)
15. (5, 10)	15. (2, 13)	15. (6, 9)	15. (8, 6)	15. (11, 21)		15. (9, 19)
16. (8, 4)	16. (1, 14)	16. (6, 1)	16. (5, 4)	16. (12, 22)		16. (2, 17)
17. (9, 3)	17. (1, 15)	17. (8, 1)	17. (2, 4)	17. (13, 22)		17. (4, 24)
18. (8, 2)	18. (0, 14)	18. (7, 2)	18. (5, 1)	18. (15, 20)		18. (6, 18)
19. (8, 1)	19. (0, 13)	19. (7, 9)	19. (8, 1)	19. (15, 19)		19. (3, 18)
20. (10, 2)	20. (2, 9)	20. (8, 9)	20. (10, 2)	20. (14, 18)		20. (4, 21)
21. (11, 1)	21. (3, 18)	21. (8, 2)	21. (12, 1)	21. (7, 12)		21. (5, 18)
22. (12, 1)	22. (5, 7)	22. (10, 2)	22. (15,1)	22. (6, 13)		22. (12, 18)
23. (10, 5)	23. (11, 7)	23. (9, 3)	23. (18, 4)	23. (6, 15)		23. (14, 24)
24. (9, 8)	24. (14, 10)	24. (9, 9)	24. (15, 4)	24. (7, 16)		24. (16, 17)
25. (8, 10)	25. (14, 13)	25. (1, 9)	25. (12, 6)	25. (10, 16)		25. (13, 18)
26. (8, 12)	26. (13, 16)	26. (2, 12)	26. (11, 8)	26. (11, 15)		26. (14, 21)
27. (9, 14)	27. (14, 17)	27. (3, 10)	27. (13, 11)	27. (11, 13)		27. (15, 18)
28. (8, 15)	28. (16, 16)	28. (4, 14)	28. (14, 14)	28 (10, 12)		28. (5, 15)
29. (9, 14)	29. (7, 7)	29. (5, 10)	29. (14, 15)	29. (4, 13)		29. (6, 15)
30. (10, 14)	30. (7, 5)	30. (6, 14)	30. (14, 14)	30. (2, 12)		30. (7, 14)
31. (10, 15)	31. (8, 4)	31. (7, 10)	31. (15, 13)	31. (1, 10)		31. (7, 12)
32. (9, 17)	32. (9, 4)	32. (8, 14)	32. (16, 11)	32. (1, 8)		32. (6, 11)
33. (8, 18)	33. (9, 5)	33. (9, 10)	33. (16, 14)	33. (2, 7)		33. (5, 11)
34. (11, 8)	34. (8, 5)	34. (10, 14)	34. (5, 20)	34. (3, 8)		34. (4, 12)
35. (13, 8)	35. (8, 7)	35. (11, 9)	35. (3, 19)	35. (4, 10)		35. (4, 14)
36. (11, 10)	36. (10, 7)	36. (12, 13)	36. (1, 17)	36. (4, 7)		36. (5, 15)
37. (11, 11)	37. (10, 6)	37. (13, 10)	37. (0, 14)	37. (13,13)		37. (5, 14)
38. (12, 12)	38. (11, 5)	38. (14, 15)	38. (0, 12)	38. (15, 12)		38. (6, 14)
39. (13, 11)	39. (12, 5)		39. (1, 9)	39. (16, 10)		39. (6, 12)
40. (13, 10)	40. (12, 6)		40. (2, 11)	40. (16, 8)		40. (5, 12)
41. (11, 8)	41. (11, 6)		41. (3, 12)	41. (15, 7)		41. (5, 14)
42. (13, 17)	42. (11, 7)		42. (6, 11)	42. (14, 8)		42. (12, 15)
43. (15, 17)				43. (13, 10)		43. (13, 15)
44. (13, 19)				44. (13, 7)		44. (14, 14)
45. (13, 20)				45. (11, 7)		45. (14, 12)
46. (14, 21)				46. (10, 5)		46. (13, 11)
47. (15, 20)				47. (10, 3)		47. (12, 11)
48. (15, 19)				48. (11, 1)		48. (11, 12)
49. (13,17)				49. (14, 1)		49. (11, 14)
				50. (15, 3)		50. (12,15)
				51. (15, 5)		51. (12, 14)
				52. (14, 7)		52. (12, 12)
				53. (11, 7)		53. (13, 12)

© Essential Resources Educational Publishers Ltd, 2008

Completed co-ordinates

Level: Medium	Level: Medium	Level: Medium	Level: Medium	Level: Medium	Level: Medium	Level: Medium
Activity 6 Cat (cont.)	Activity 7 Caterpillar	Activity 8 Dinosaur	Activity 8 Dinosaur (cont.)	Activity 9 Dog	Activity 9 Dog (cont.)	Activity 10 Elephant
54. (13, 14)	1. (9, 21)	1. (15, 10)	55. (8, 9)	1. (10, 22)	55. (2, 7)	1. (4, 12)
55. (12, 14)	2. (8, 23)	2. (14, 9)	56. (6, 9)	2. (9, 21)	56. (2, 5)	2. (3, 13)
56. (5, 5)	3. (7, 24)	3. (13, 7)	57. (7, 11)	3. (8, 18)	57. (3, 4)	3. (3, 16)
57. (7, 3)	4. (6, 24)	4. (9, 5)	58. (5, 11)	4. (7, 17)	58. (9, 4)	4. (5, 18)
58. (11, 3)	5. (4, 23)	5. (7, 5)	59. (6, 13)	5. (7, 15)	59. (9, 5)	5. (5, 19)
59. (13, 5)	6. (3, 21)	6. (5, 6)	60. (4, 14)	6. (9, 13)	60. (8, 6)	6. (4, 20)
60. (9, 3)	7. (3, 20)	7. (6, 4)	61. (6, 16)	7. (12, 13)	61. (5, 6)	7. (1, 21)
61. (9, 7)	8. (4, 19)	8. (6, 3)	62. (4, 17)	8. (14, 15)	62. (7, 6)	8. (1, 22)
62. (7, 9)	9. (6, 18)	9. (5, 2)	63. (7, 18)	9. (14, 17)	63. (8, 7)	9. (5, 21)
63. (9, 10)	10. (9, 16)	10. (4, 3)	64. (6, 19)	10. (13, 18)	64. (8, 9)	10. (6, 20)
64. (11, 9)	11. (5, 12)	11. (2, 4)	65. (8, 20)	11. (12, 21)	65. (6, 10)	11. (7, 18)
65. (9, 7)	12. (4, 10)	12. (1, 6)		12. (11, 22)	66. (2, 7)	12. (7, 17)
66. (0, 11)	13. (5, 8)	13. (2, 8)		13. (10, 22)	67. (2, 9)	13. (8, 18)
67. (6, 8)	14. (10, 4)	14. (7, 8)		14. (9, 21)	68. (3, 11)	14. (9, 15)
68. (1, 3)	15. (10, 1)	15. (8, 9)		15. (8, 21)	69. (3, 13)	15. (11, 15)
69. (6, 8)	16. (12, 0)	16. (7, 11)		16. (5, 20)	70. (2, 16)	16. (13, 16)
70. (0, 6)	17. (13, 2)	17. (6, 12)		17. (3, 19)	71. (3, 16)	17. (14, 16)
71. (18, 11)	18. (13, 6)	18. (6, 17)		18. (2, 18)	72. (4, 14)	18. (16, 17)
72. (12, 8)	19. (10, 9)	19. (7, 18)		19. (2, 17)	73. (4, 10)	19. (16, 15)
73. (17, 3)	20. (10, 11)	20. (8, 20)		20. (4, 16)	74. (8, 6)	20. (14, 15)
74. (12, 8)	21. (13, 13)	21. (7, 21)		21. (5, 16)	75. (10, 6)	21. (12, 13)
75. (18, 6)	22. (14, 15)	22. (5, 21)		22. (7, 17)		22. (12, 12)
	23. (12, 19)	23. (3, 20)		23. (12, 21)		23. (13, 10)
	24. (10, 21)	24. (1, 17)		24. (14, 20)		24. (13, 8)
	25. (9, 21)	25. (0, 17)		25. (15, 18)		25. (12, 6)
	26. (8, 23)	26. (1, 20)		26. (16, 16)		26. (11, 5)
	27. (7, 21)	27. (2, 21)		27. (17, 15)		27. (12, 6)
	28. (6, 18)	28. (5, 23)		28. (17, 13)		28. (14, 6)
	29. (9, 21)	29. (9, 23)		29. (16, 12)		29. (15, 7)
	30. (9, 17)	30. (12, 22)		30. (14, 12)		30. (15, 6)
	31. (11, 19)	31. (13, 20)		31. (13, 13)		31. (14, 5)
	32. (10, 16)	32. (15, 20)		32. (13, 14)		32. (12, 6)
	33. (13, 16)	33. (16, 19)		33. (8, 16)		33. (14, 5)
	34. (9, 15)	34. (16, 17)		34. (9, 14)		34. (16, 6)
	35. (12, 14)	35. (14, 17)		35. (12, 14)		35. (16, 4)
	36. (7, 14)	36. (12, 14)		36. (13, 16)		36. (12, 4)
	37. (10, 11)	37. (10, 14)		37. (12, 13)		37. (10, 3)
	38. (5, 11)	38. (14, 17)		38. (13, 11)		38. (9, 3)
	39. (10, 10)	39. (15, 14)		39. (13, 8)		39. (7, 4)
	40. (7, 8)	40. (15, 13)		40. (14, 6)		40. (6, 5)
	41. (10, 9)	41. (15, 17)		41. (15, 5)		41. (5, 7)
	42. (9, 6)	42. (16, 16)		42. (15, 4)		42. (5, 9)
	43. (11, 8)	43. (16, 14)		43. (11, 4)		43. (13, 14)
	44. (10, 4)	44. (15, 14)		44. (9, 8)		44. (14, 14)
	45. (12, 6)	45. (14, 13)		45. (9, 9)		45. (15, 15)
	46. (10, 3)	46. (15, 13)		46. (11, 9)		46. (15, 13)
	47. (13, 2)	47. (17, 12)		47. (11, 8)		47. (12, 13)
		48. (17, 9)		48. (12, 6)		48. (5, 13)
		49. (15, 10)		49. (13, 5)		49. (4, 12)
		50. (14, 10)		50. (13, 4)		50. (4, 10)
		51. (15, 10)		51. (9, 13)		51. (5, 9)
		52. (16, 9)		52. (6, 12)		52. (8, 9)
		53. (16, 7)		53. (4, 10)		53. (9, 10)
		54. (14, 8)		54. (3, 9)		54. (9, 12)

Level: Medium	Level: Medium	Level: Medium	Level: Medium	Level: Medium	Level: Medium	Level: Medium
Activity 10 Elephant (cont.)	Activity 11 Frog	Activity 11 Frog (cont.)	Activity 12 Horse	Activity 13 Koala	Activity 13 Koala (cont.)	Activity 14 Tiger
55. (8, 13)	1. (7, 5)	55. (11, 6)	1. (7, 13)	1. (9, 13)	55. (8, 9)	1. (4, 4)
56. (6, 13)	2. (5, 4)	56. (12, 9)	2. (8, 12)	2. (8, 14)	56. (9, 10)	2. (5, 3)
57. (5, 12)	3. (2, 3)	57. (12, 10)	3. (9, 12)	3. (7, 16)	57. (10, 10)	3. (5, 1)
58. (5, 10)	4. (3, 4)	58. (5, 20)	4. (10, 13)	4. (6, 17)	58. (12, 9)	4. (4, 0)
59. (8, 10)	5. (1, 4)	59. (5, 21)	5. (12, 14)	5. (5, 19)	59. (12, 8)	5. (1, 0)
60. (8, 12)	6. (2, 5)	60. (6, 22)	6. (16, 14)	6. (5, 21)	60. (9,13)	6. (2, 1)
61. (7, 13)	7. (1, 6)	61. (7, 21)	7. (17, 15)	7. (6, 22)	61. (5, 13)	7. (2, 3)
62. (9, 3)	8. (4, 6)	62. (11, 21)	8. (17, 16)	8. (8, 22)	62. (4, 12)	8. (1, 4)
63. (11, 2)	9. (2, 8)	63. (12, 22)	9. (16, 15)	9. (9, 21)	63. (5, 11)	9. (2, 4)
	10. (1, 10)	64. (13, 21)	10. (9, 15)	10. (10, 22)	64. (6, 11)	10. (3, 5)
	11. (2, 12)	65. (13, 20)	11. (5, 18)	11. (11, 22)	65. (9,10)	11. (4, 7)
	12. (3, 12)	66. (6, 19)	12. (6, 20)	12. (12, 21)	66. (2, 24)	12. (5, 15)
	13. (5, 10)	67. (7, 17)	13. (7, 21)	13. (13, 22)	67. (5, 13)	13. (6, 17)
	14. (5, 13)	68. (8, 16)	14. (7, 22)	14. (15, 22)	68. (1, 24)	14. (7, 18)
	15. (6, 15)	69. (10, 16)	15. (6, 22)	15. (16, 21)	69. (4, 13)	15. (9, 19)
	16. (4, 16)	70. (11, 17)	16. (4, 21)	16. (16, 19)	70. (5, 11)	16. (13, 19)
	17. (4, 19)	71. (12, 19)	17. (2, 19)	17. (15, 17)	71. (6, 9)	17. (14, 20)
	18. (8, 21)	72. (7, 6)	18. (3, 16)	18. (14, 16)	72. (6, 11)	18. (14, 21)
	19. (10, 21)	73. (7, 5)	19. (5, 10)	19. (13, 14)	73. (7, 9)	19. (13, 22)
	20. (14, 19)	74. (11, 6)	20. (4, 7)	20. (12, 13)	74. (8, 5)	20. (14, 22)
	21. (14, 16)	75. (11, 5)	21. (5, 4)	21. (9, 13)	75. (9, 2)	21. (15, 21)
	22. (12, 15)		22. (6, 3)	22. (7, 21)	76. (9, 5)	22. (14, 19)
	23. (13, 13)		23. (9, 4)	23. (8, 20)	77. (10, 2)	23. (12, 18)
	24. (13, 10)		24. (10, 5)	24. (8, 19)		24. (9, 18)
	25. (15, 12)		25. (12, 4)	25. (7, 18)		25. (8, 17)
	26. (16, 12)		26. (16, 4)	26. (6, 19)		26. (11, 17)
	27. (17, 10)		27. (17, 5)	27. (6, 20)		27. (14, 18)
	28. (16, 8)		28. (17, 6)	28. (7, 21)		28. (16, 17)
	29. (14, 6)		29. (16, 5)	29. (14, 21)		29. (16, 16)
	30. (17, 6)		30. (12, 5)	30. (15, 20)		30. (14, 17)
	31. (16, 5)		31. (10, 6)	31. (15, 19)		31. (12, 15)
	32. (17, 4)		32. (9, 7)	32. (14, 18)		32. (9, 16)
	33. (15, 4)		33. (7, 7)	33. (13, 19)		33. (11, 15)
	34. (16, 3)		34. (6, 6)	34. (13, 20)		34. (15, 15)
	35. (13, 4)		35. (9, 7)	35. (14, 21)		35. (17, 14)
	36. (11, 5)		36. (10, 10)	36. (9, 15)		36. (17, 13)
	37. (6, 10)		37. (10, 13)	37. (10, 14)		37. (15, 14)
	38. (6, 9)		38. (14, 13)	38. (11, 14)		38. (13, 13)
	39. (7, 6)		39. (15, 14)	39. (12, 15)		39. (10, 12)
	40. (8, 5)		40. (10, 6)	40. (13, 14)		40. (8, 12)
	41. (6, 2)		41. (15, 6)	41. (14, 13)		41. (11, 12)
	42. (7, 3)		42. (16, 7)	42. (15, 11)		42. (10, 7)
	43. (7, 2)		43. (16, 6)	43. (16, 8)		43. (15, 7)
	44. (8, 3)		44. (15, 5)	44. (16, 7)		44. (16, 6)
	45. (8, 2)		45. (5, 4)	45. (15, 5)		45. (16, 4)
	46. (9, 4)		46. (6, 2)	46. (13, 4)		46. (15, 5)
	47. (9, 9)		47. (10, 2)	47. (11, 4)		47. (13, 5)
	48. (9, 4)		48. (13, 3)	48. (9, 5)		48. (9, 4)
	49. (10, 2)		49. (6, 3)	49. (7, 5)		49. (7, 3)
	50. (10, 3)		50. (2, 18)	50. (6, 6)		50. (5, 3)
	51. (11, 2)		51. (1, 19)	51. (5, 8)		51. (9, 7)
	52. (11, 3)		52. (2, 19)	52. (6, 9)		52. (13, 6)
	53. (12, 2)		53. (1, 20)	53. (7, 9)		53. (15, 6)
	54. (10, 5)		54. (2, 20)	54. (8, 8)		54. (16, 5)

Level: Medium	Level: Hard	Level: Hard	Level: Hard	Level: Hard	Level: Hard	Level: Hard
Activity 14 Tiger (cont.)	Activity 15 Bee	Activity 15 Bee (cont.)	Activity 16 Butterfly	Activity 16 Butterfly (cont.)	Activity 17 Ladybird	Activity 17 Ladybird (cont.)
55. (4, 5)	1. (7, 16)	55. (4, 7)	1. (7, 18)	55. (5, 8)	1. (8, 19)	55. (6, 11)
56. (5, 5)	2. (7, 18)	56. (4, 6)	2. (10, 14)	56. (4, 7)	2. (6, 17)	56. (4, 9)
57. (7, 4)	3. (8, 19)	57. (10, 13)	3. (10, 6)	57. (4, 6)	3. (5, 15)	57. (6, 7)
58. (5, 6)	4. (9, 19)	58. (14, 11)	4. (9, 5)	58. (5, 6)	4. (3, 13)	58. (8, 9)
59. (9, 5)	5. (10, 18)	59. (14, 10)	5. (8, 6)	59. (6, 8)	5. (2, 11)	59. (6, 11)
60. (5, 8)	6. (10, 16)	60. (11, 11)	6. (8, 14)	60. (15, 16)	6. (2, 5)	60. (12, 11)
61. (7, 7)	7. (7, 16)	61. (13, 7)	7. (11, 18)	61. (13, 16)	7. (3, 3)	61. (10, 9)
62. (5, 10)	8. (6, 15)	62. (13, 6)	8. (8, 14)	62. (11, 14)	8. (5, 1)	62. (12, 7)
63. (9, 9)	9. (6, 14)	63. (7, 5)	9. (4, 18)	63. (11, 12)	9. (7, 0)	63. (14, 9)
64. (5, 12)	10. (7, 13)	64. (10, 5)	10. (1, 18)	64. (14, 12)	10. (11, 0)	64. (12, 11)
65. (7, 11)	11. (10, 13)	65. (6, 6)	11. (1, 16)	65. (15, 15)	11. (13, 1)	65. (4, 7)
66. (10, 10)	12. (11, 14)	66. (11, 6)	12. (2, 12)	66. (15, 16)	12. (15, 3)	66. (3, 6)
67. (6, 14)	13. (11, 15)	67. (6, 8)	13. (4, 10)	67. (14, 15)	13. (16, 5)	67. (4, 5)
68. (9, 14)	14. (10, 16)	68. (11, 8)	14. (8, 11)	68. (13, 15)	14. (16, 11)	68. (5, 6)
69. (11, 13)	15. (7, 13)	69. (6, 9)	15. (4, 10)	69. (12, 14)	15. (15, 13)	69. (4, 7)
70. (6, 16)	16. (6, 11)	70. (11, 9)	16. (2, 8)	70. (12, 13)	16. (13, 15)	70. (7, 4)
71. (8, 16)	17. (6, 6)	71. (6, 11)	17. (1, 5)	71. (13, 13)	17. (12, 17)	71. (6, 3)
72. (9, 15)	18. (8, 4)	72. (11, 11)	18. (4, 3)	72. (14, 15)	18. (10, 19)	72. (7, 2)
73. (9, 19)	19. (8, 2)	73. (7, 12)	19. (6, 3)	73. (11, 9)	19. (8, 19)	73. (8, 3)
74. (10, 18)	20. (9, 2)	74. (10, 12)	20. (8, 6)	74. (11, 7)	20. (7, 21)	74. (7, 4)
75. (11, 19)	21. (9, 4)	75. (7, 17)	21. (10, 14)	75. (13, 5)	21. (6, 21)	75. (14, 7)
76. (12, 18)	22. (11, 6)	76. (8, 17)	22. (14, 18)	76. (15, 5)	22. (10, 19)	76. (13, 6)
	23. (11, 11)	77. (8, 19)	23. (17, 18)	77. (15, 8)	23. (11, 21)	77. (14, 5)
	24. (10, 13)	78. (10, 17)	24. (17, 16)	78. (13, 9)	24. (12, 21)	78. (15, 6)
	25. (7, 16)	79. (9, 17)	25. (16, 12)	79. (11, 9)	25. (3, 19)	79. (14, 7)
	26. (2, 20)	80. (9, 19)	26. (14, 10)	80. (12, 8)	26. (3, 18)	80. (11, 4)
	27. (0, 20)		27. (10, 11)	81. (13, 6)	27. (5, 15)	81. (10, 3)
	28. (0, 15)		28. (14, 10)	82. (14, 6)	28. (13, 15)	82. (11, 2)
	29. (7, 13)		29. (16, 8)	83. (14, 7)	29. (15, 18)	83. (12, 3)
	30. (6, 15)		30. (17, 5)	84. (13, 8)	30. (15, 19)	84. (11, 4)
	31. (0, 18)		31. (14, 3)	85. (12, 8)	31. (9, 15)	
	32. (10, 16)		32. (12, 3)		32. (9, 0)	
	33. (16, 20)		33. (10, 6)		33. (4, 14)	
	34. (18, 20)		34. (3, 16)		34. (0, 11)	
	35. (18, 15)		35. (3, 15)		35. (0, 10)	
	36. (10, 13)		36. (4, 12)		36. (14, 14)	
	37. (11, 15)		37. (7, 12)		37. (18, 11)	
	38. (18, 18)		38. (7, 14)		38. (18, 10)	
	39. (7, 16)		39. (5, 16)		39. (2, 5)	
	40. (6, 18)		40. (3, 16)		40. (0, 2)	
	41. (6, 19)		41. (4, 15)		41. (0, 1)	
	42. (10, 16)		42. (5, 13)		42. (16, 5)	
	43. (11, 18)		43. (6, 13)		43. (18, 2)	
	44. (11, 19)		44. (6, 14)		44. (18, 1)	
	45. (8, 19)		45. (5, 15)		45. (6, 14)	
	46. (7, 20)		46. (4, 15)		46. (5, 13)	
	47. (7, 21)		47. (7, 9)		47. (6, 12)	
	48. (9, 19)		48. (5, 9)		48. (7, 13)	
	49. (10, 20)		49. (3, 8)		49. (6, 14)	
	50. (10, 21)		50. (3, 5)		50. (12, 14)	
	51. (7, 13)		51. (5, 5)		51. (11, 13)	
	52. (3, 11)		52. (7, 7)		52. (12, 12)	
	53. (3, 10)		53. (7, 9)		53. (13, 13)	
	54. (6, 11)		54. (6, 8)		54. (12, 14)	